C000136259

Jean McSorley was born in Barr̶ ̶ ̶ ̶ ̶ ̶ ̶ ̶ ̶ ̶ ̶ ̶ ̶ ̶
1958. She is one of the founder m̶ ̶ ̶ ̶ ̶ ̶ ̶ ̶ ̶ ̶ ̶ ̶ ̶ ̶
to a Radioactive Environment, w̶ ̶ ̶ ̶ ̶ ̶ ̶ ̶ ̶ ̶ ̶ ̶ ̶ ̶
past ten years the group has cam̶ ̶ ̶ ̶ ̶ ̶ ̶ ̶ ̶ ̶ ̶ ̶ ̶
nuclear waste to Sellafield; for the ̶ ̶ ̶ ̶ ̶ ̶ ̶ ̶ ̶ ̶ ̶ ̶ ̶
ges from Sellafield; for just comp̶ ̶ ̶ ̶ ̶ ̶ ̶ ̶ ̶ ̶ ̶ ̶ ̶ ̶
who suffer ill-health effects from Sellafield; against any form of nuclear
waste dumping; for lower radiation levels from all man-made sources; for
the cessation of the use of nuclear power for both civil and military
purposes.

LIVING IN THE
SHADOW

JEAN McSORLEY

PAN BOOKS
London, Sydney and Auckland

First published in 1990 by Pan Books Ltd,
Cavaye Place, London SW10 9PG

9 8 7 6 5 4 3 2 1

© Jean McSorley 1990

ISBN 0 330 31331 2

Maps by Ken Smith
Photoset by Parker Typesetting Service, Leicester
Printed and bound by
Richard Clay Ltd, Bungay, Suffolk

This book is dedicated to my mother Patricia McSorley, my sister, Moira, brothers Paul and Terry, and David Smith, without whose love and support it would never have been written.

CONTENTS

MAPS

Acknowledgements

My sincerest thanks, first and foremost, to all those who were interviewed. I would like to acknowledge the help of Nick May, who helped in the collection of some of the interviews. My thanks to Simon Boxer and Phil Reed who took on so much extra work to free me for the task of writing and to Elaine Lawrence and Phil Cade of Greenpeace for their trust in my ability to see this project through.

Over the ten years of campaigning I have had much encouragement in my work. Some of it is given in a personal capacity, from friends and relations. Then there is the help from the many volunteers who have asked for nothing in return for their work. Although this book is not about them I think it only fair to give them credit. Therefore I am taking the opportunity now as it is rare that one gets a chance to publicly acknowledge all the help and support given so freely and so unselfishly. My thanks then to: Patricia Appleton, Willem Beekman, Irene Brunskill, Mavis Coward, Martyn Day, Martin Forwood, Sonia Gibson, Hans Guyt, Matt Kelly, Paul McGhee, Janet Scott, Harry Smith and his late wife Pat, Terry Smith, Anita Stirzaker, Peter Taylor, Jean Thompson and last, but certainly not least, Peter Wilkinson.

My gratitude also to Hilary Davies of Pan Books and her staff for being so helpful throughout all of this.

Information from local newspapers has been an invaluable source in the research of this book. I would like to acknowledge the excerpts taken from the *Whitehaven News*. I would like to stress that the newspaper does not hold either pro or anti nuclear views. My thanks also to the *North Western Evening Mail* for use of information from their newspaper.

Money from the sale of this book will go towards Cumbrians Opposed to a Radioactive Environment's Campaign and Compensation Fund. For further information contact: CORE, 98 Church Street, Barrow-in-Furness, Cumbria.

ABBREVIATIONS

AEU – Amalgamated Engineering Union
BNFL – British Nuclear Fuels Limited
CEGB – Central Electricity Generating Board
COMARE – Committee on the Medical Aspects of Radiation in the Environment
CORE – Cumbrians Opposed to a Radioactive Environment
EETPU – The Electrical, Electronic & Telecommunications and Plumbing Union
GMB – General Municipal and Boilermakers Union
ICRP – International Commission on Radiological Protection
IPCS – Institute of Professional Civil Servants
MAFF – Ministry of Agriculture, Fisheries and Food
NII – Nuclear Installations Inspectorate
NIREX – Nuclear Industry Radioactive Waste Executive
NRPB – National Radiological Protection Board
PERG – Political Ecology Research Group
UKAEA – United Kingdom Atomic Energy Authority

AGR – Advanced Gas-cooled Reactor
PWR – Pressurised Water Reactor
THORP – Thermal Oxide Reprocessing Plant

d/m – Daily Mirror
d/e – Daily Express
e/m – North Western Evening Mail
g – Guardian
n/s – New Scientist
obs – Observer
tel – Daily Telegraph
w/n – Whitehaven News

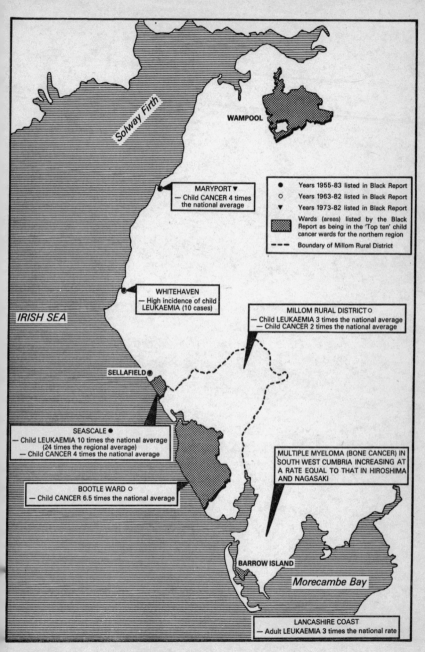

WAMPOOL

Solway Firth

MARYPOOL ▼
— Child CANCER 4 times
the national average

●   Years 1955-83 listed in Black Report
○   Years 1963-82 listed in Black Report
▼   Years 1973-82 listed in Black Report

    Wards (areas) listed by the Black
    Report as being in the 'Top ten' child
    cancer wards for the northern region

– – –   Boundary of Millom Rural District

IRISH SEA

WHITEHAVEN
— High incidence of child
LEUKAEMIA (10 cases)

MILLOM RURAL DISTRICT ○
— Child LEUKAEMIA 3 times the national average
— Child CANCER 2 times the national average

SELLAFIELD ●

SEASCALE ●
— Child LEUKAEMIA 10 times the national average
(24 times the regional average)
— Child CANCER 4 times the national average

**MULTIPLE MYELOMA (BONE CANCER) IN
SOUTH WEST CUMBRIA INCREASING AT
A RATE EQUAL TO THAT IN HIROSHIMA
AND NAGASAKI**

BOOTLE WARD ○
— Child CANCER 6.5 times the national average

BARROW ISLAND

Morecambe Bay

LANCASHIRE COAST
— Adult LEUKAEMIA 3 times the national rate

Sellafield and Surrounding Area

CHAPTER

1

A race that binds
Its body in chains and calls them Liberty,
And calls each fresh link Progress.
'Titan & Avatar', Robert Williams Buchanan

'I opened the gag-port and there it was, there was a fire at the face of the reactor.' These are the words of Mr Arthur Wilson, the 'Man Who Found the Windscale Fire'. The blaze he discovered on 10th October 1957 signalled the beginning of the world's second biggest nuclear accident.

Mr Wilson is the master of understatement. 'I can't say I thought a lot about it at the time, there was so much to do. I didn't think "Hurrah', I've found it." I rather thought, "Oh dear, now we are in a pickle." In some ways I was quite lucky because I had been on duty so long that day I was allowed home quite soon after the fire itself was discovered. It's the other poor souls I feel most sorry for, the ones who had to go in and sort out the mess. Some of them got very high doses and I'm sure things weren't recorded properly then. In fact the reaction of the management to the news that there was a fire was "Don't be so bloody daft." I don't know what they expected. For days it had been going wrong.'

'It' was the planned release of heat from No.1 of the twin Plutonium Piles at Windscale which supplied Britain's first nuclear weapon material. By today's standards the reactors were badly designed and hastily erected. Many problems had not been foreseen, like the heat build-up which occurred from time to time in the graphite surrounding the hot nuclear fuel in the reactor. This graphite acted as a 'moderator' by soaking up the excess energy coming off the fuel as it was burnt in the reactor. The heat caused the graphite to expand in size and so had to be got rid of by blowing air across the graphite and allowing the heat to escape

1

from a 400 foot chimney. The operation had been successfully undertaken twice prior to 1957.

'I can't say that any of us were very much worried about what happened. We thought we were undertaking a routine operation. I was there at the time because I was an instrument technician and it was my job to fit the thermocouples to the reactor. Thermocouples are sophisticated thermometers which kept track of the heat build-up in the reactor. We'd actually started the energy release on the Monday and by Wednesday morning the temperature should have gone down. But we could see from the gauges that the temperature was still rising. There was a sense of "what next", but not in a worried sort of way, just what do we do to sort it out. On the Thursday morning there was no way of knowing the temperature as some of the thermocouples had burnt off, we'd tried attaching new ones, but they burnt off too. We were stood on the charge hoist and someone suggested that we actually had a look at the reactor itself. It didn't seem such a bad idea. There were holes which were used to put the fuel in, you could also see inside the reactor through them. We thought "what the hell." I was first to look and then I saw the thin wisps of flame, nothing very spectacular, but then I suppose it was spectacular enough in itself.'

Arthur Wilson, born in Millom, started work at Sellafield in 1951 after he left the army. He worked in a number of the buildings on site. He recalls how inefficient the health physics people were in those early years. 'One day I was called in because I had a sample of urine contaminated with plutonium. I remember feeling quite worried about this for days, it was the first time I had cause to worry. Like most people I was in the thick of things. I enjoyed work. We were leading a new technology and I was part of it. There was a challenge to invent, to get round problems. When the results of the second test came back I was relieved to know that I was clear. The health physics people said my sample had been cross-contaminated. That was it. I never asked by who or what and they never told me. It wasn't for some time that I thought about my contamination and then I said to myself, "That's a devil of a thing to happen." Did someone else get the all-clear, but in fact were contaminated? I decided to test them. I took my radiation badge and sat it on top of a very radioactive source in the separation plant. I knew it was radioactive because I had a Geiger counter with me. I then went off and did a job in a nice clean area. I came back, got the badge, handed it in and waited. Not a beep out of them. That badge must have shown I was over-exposed, there's no way round it. But it shows what we had to suffer in the early days. I suppose the only excuse is that the world was new then, or at least it felt that way after the war.'

Even before the 1957 accident Arthur Wilson had begun to notice pains and loss of feeling in his legs. By that time he had already been contaminated in various routine operations. On one occasion he had had to open a plate on the separation route in order to move one of the highly radioactive fuel rods that had stuck in the processing machinery. 'I remember whipping open this "hatch" and seeing this fuel rod only some five foot from me. I belted it quickly and slammed the lid shut.' Other dangerous operations included going into the base of the reactor and pushing the hot spent fuel rods into the cooling pond that had landed on a side-ledge by mistake. As he became more and more ill Arthur Wilson began to question the company doctors. He was told that they had no idea what was afflicting him, but that it wasn't radiation linked. 'How could they say they didn't know what it was in one breath and then exclude radiation in the next?' wonders Arthur. 'I wasn't out to skin them, I just wanted to know. I was only thirty-six. I was being paid off, I knew I'd never work again. Well, never do normal work again. I could only walk using sticks. They gave me £400 superannuation. I've never seen or heard of them since, not even a Christmas card from the unions. Perhaps they regard me as a bit of an embarrassment. But I'm an old man, what are they afraid of?'

Arthur finished working at the plant in 1961. Photographs of him taken at that time show a handsome, fit looking man. In some of them he is pictured with the telescopes he designed and built. The little pieces of carpentry he worked on for home furnishings now lie around the floor of one room of his house. He will never complete the work. His health has now deteriorated to the point where he is crippled and can only use his right arm, and that gets tired easily. Arthur lives alone in a council bungalow. Although he is wheelchair-bound he values his independence. In 1988 he spent the last of his savings on a motorised wheelchair as he did not want to live in a residential home. His mind is still alert and his spirit is strong. In 1967 a neuro-surgeon examined Arthur. He reported that he believed his illness could be radiation linked. Although this was later withdrawn. CORE tried to get Arthur's case looked at again. Because he does not have a cancer he cannot claim under BNFL's compensation scheme. Eventually we had to abandon Arthur's claim as he could not face the pain of going through more tests on his spine.

Tom Touhy was the deputy manager of the Windscale & Calder Works at the time of the 1957 fire. A chemist by training, during the war he spent part of his time at Drigg and Sellafield when they were explosives factories. After the war he was offered a job in the newly founded nuclear industry. As Touhy says, 'Who wants to make TNT when the atom bomb has gone off?'

After a two-year spell at Springfields, BNFL's fuel fabrication plant, Touhy became deputy manager at Windscale and then general manager in 1958. In 1949 he took charge of the Windscale Plutonium Piles and in 1950 was asked to start up the plutonium finishing plant which made the finished metal for nuclear weapons. 'We made the first small billet of plutonium, 142 grammes I remember, about the size of a ten-pence piece. I broke down the first reaction vessel myself, with these hands, I was the first man to handle and see a piece of entirely British-made plutonium.'

Touhy was in charge of on-the-spot operations for dealing with the fire and remembers quite vividly what took place. 'I was at home when the thing started. I got a phone call from the then general manager, Henry Davey, who said "Pile Number One is on fire." "Christ, you don't mean the core?" "Yes, can you come in?" Naturally I told him I would. My wife and children were all in bed with Asian flu. I said, "Look there's trouble at Windscale." She asked "When will I see you?" and I said I hadn't a clue.

'I went in and didn't go and see Davey in his office. I went straight to the source of the trouble, as I always did. On the charge hoist of the reactor a team of men were busy trying to isolate the fire by discharging a ring of fuel around about where they thought the fire was located so it couldn't spread.'

Because these reactors were the first they were quite different from those used today – a fact that helped enormously in dealing with the blaze. The metal fuel rods in the old reactors were pushed in horizontally, not lowered in from the top as in modern ones. The reactor was a series of graphite blocks and 'fuel channels', which looked like a chequer board from the front. To get access to the reactor face you pulled plugs out of what was called the charge wall, which was about four and a half feet thick reinforced concrete.

The fuel was simply pushed into the reactor through the channels. In between the wall and the face of the reactor was an air duct through which the piles were air-cooled. The process of putting fuel in or pushing it out was known as charging and discharging. Old fuel was discharged at the back by pushing fresh fuel in from the front. A special machine, the charge machine, had been designed to do this job. Attached to the charge machine was a tube which spanned the air duct. Each plug gave access to only four fuel channels at a time. The charge machine was meant to be able to locate each of the four channels in turn. However, this did not work reliably and instead ordinary household bamboo drain rods were used to put fuel in or push it out. In those days there were no TV cameras inside the reactor to tell workers what was going on, so they had to actually look inside. The huge piece of machinery from which all of this was done was known as the charge hoist. This could be moved up and down the front of the 80 foot-high reactor.

Touhy explains: 'I spent most of my time on the charge hoist where the men were trying to put this ring around the fire. When we'd got a ring of empty channels right around where the fire was, I decided to try and discharge some of the burning fuel channels. I got the men to pull out various of these plugs and looked into the reactor, which is not recommended under normal circumstances. By having various plugs pulled out I defined the area roughly where the fire was. The fuel was glowing red at this stage. Normally there wouldn't be any sign of heat at all.'

This was not a nuclear reaction. 'It was like a fire in a grate, except we had burning graphite and burning uranium. One of the troubles was the only coolant we had at this stage was air, and air and fire are not very good companions. You had to keep a certain amount of air going through the system fans because of the ventilation to the charge hoist, where the men were working. If you interfered with that you could get a lot of contamination coming back whenever you pulled one of the plugs out. Also if you took off all the cooling we didn't know how much residual heat [known as Wigner energy] was still in the graphite. We'd got a nice little fire in the middle of this and if you supply no coolant at all to the surrounding graphite and there's still Wigner energy you can have a much bigger fire on your hands.'

The management faced severe problems. 'Drain rods were no good whatever for trying to discharge the burning fuel because they were ordinary drain rods made of bamboo. So we got steel rods and tried to push this stuff out but a lot of the fuel was in a molten state which you obviously couldn't push through.

'I had a gang of men sort of heaving on the end of each pole. Very little was happening. I remember the poles were coming back absolutely red hot. Individual fuel elements were only a foot long and they sat on T-shaped pieces of graphite called graphite boats. On one occasion when a rod came back onto the charge hoist there was a red hot graphite boat came with it which dropped onto the charge hoist. I remember kicking it over the side and molten metal, which must have been uranium, was also dripping off. We decided to abandon this as being hopeless and kept trying to discharge the burning fuel and make a bigger ring around where the fire was.

'One way of trying to define how bad things were was to go right up the top of the reactor and look down the back of it. We had to go up 80 feet and there were no lifts in those days. It doesn't sound very much but if you're carrying 35 pounds of breathing equipment on your back and you've got a full face respirator by the time you get to the top your chin is swimming in your own sweat.'

At the back of the reactor was the 'discharge duct' where the used fuel was pushed out of the reactor. This fuel fell down into water which contained bogeys. Above this discharge duct there were four holes through the top of the biological shield. They were normally plugged, but in the shut-down state, leading up to carrying out the Wigner release, these plugs had been taken out and they were merely steel discs on top. These could be taken out and the men could look down into the duct. When Touhy first looked into his duct there was no sign of fire.

'I alternated my time between the charge hoist where the discharge operations were going on and going up to the roof to look down these inspection holes at the back to see if I could see any sign of the fire. First there was a red glow as the fire was spreading down the channel, then there were flames coming out the back, then there were massive flames shooting right across the discharge duct and impinging on the concrete wall at the back of the duct. Here was I looking at this knowing that the civil engineers had said that if that wall exceeded 600 degrees centigrade the roof on which I was standing could possibly collapse. It wasn't a pleasant thought.

'We'd got to think of some alternative cooling to the air which we were having to keep supplying so we could live on the charge hoist. But we had to keep the graphite cool to some extent. I was as reluctant as anybody else to use water. We decided that we'd have a go with carbon dioxide. Because Calder Hall was cooled with carbon dioxide a tanker with 25 tons of liquid carbon dioxide had come into Calder that day. However, because of experiments we had already done we did not think it would work.

'We had difficulties with the hoses to the face of the reactor. Because the charge hoist could be located at all sorts of levels the way to get up there was a service lift. You can't shut the door with the hose in the way. However, there was an escape ladder from the charge hoist, in case the service lift failed, and we managed to get the hose up the escape ladder onto the charge hoist. I had some men pull a plug out of the wall and put this tube in, spanning the gap which wasn't just glowing red hot, it was flaming all over the place. I watched what happened, again a rather unhealthy thing to do, but there was no other way of finding out what was going to happen except looking at the channels. It was exactly as I said, nothing happened, it just went on burning as merrily as before.

'The only other thing we had available in any quantity was water and this was a sort of last resort. If you mix steam and graphite you make a gas which is a mixture of hydrogen and carbon monoxide, which can explode violently, so it is not a very nice mix. Anyway, we made the decision to use water and again setting hoses up was difficult.'

The reactor had holes in it in which could be placed containers for making various other radioactive materials, such as Polonium-210, which was used as a trigger for nuclear weapons. The hoses carrying the water were attached at one end to a fire engine and at the other to tubes placed in the isotope holes. Tom Touhy had gone on site around four in the afternoon; it was now five in the morning.

'By this time, of course, the charge hoist was very radioactive because of the molten irradiated uranium dripping on the carpet, so to speak. The radiation levels were building up all the time. We had the men on the charge hoist in relays so that none of them really got a very big exposure. I got by far and away the biggest exposure that night. You had to wear a mask so you didn't breathe any of the dust, that was absolutely vital. By seven o'clock in the morning we were ready to put water in the system. But there was a problem as the people on early shifts were arriving and then other staff continued to arrive until about nine o'clock.

'Not quite knowing what was going to happen when the water went on we couldn't turn it on until we were assured everybody was under cover. I decided not to fire the water directly into the burning uranium because I was frightened of an explosion arising from the cold water hitting this very hot metal. I thought, I'll not put it on direct. I chose places for laying the hoses which were about two feet above where I knew the fire was.

'The graphite core of the reactor is not solid. It's made up of lots and lots of individual blocks with gaps in between to allow for expansion of the graphite. I knew that the water would trickle down and so get at the fire. The fire chief, a man called Bill Crone, was very good. He and his team were outside and the chief engineer, Donald Ireland, acted as a sort of runner between myself and the fire chief. I asked for 30 pounds of pressure on the water supply and sat down at the entrance to the service lift, as near to the charge hoist as I reasonably could, listening for any horrible noises. Well, there weren't any at 30 pounds, so after about ten minutes I asked for 60 pounds and listened again, then 90 and then 120, which was full pressure. There were no bumps in the night, as it were.

'Outside you couldn't see a lot from the fire itself. There was a sort of heat haze over the chimney, before we put the water on, you could see the air shimmering. That was the first time we'd ever seen anything coming out of the chimney. No real smoke, just a sort of heat haze. Of course, when the water went on we immediately produced steam so the thing was steaming. Then I wondered whether we were making full use of the water or whether in fact a lot of it, with the pressure, was coming straight through the channels out the back. I went up on the roof yet again, for the umpteenth time, looked down the inspection holes and sure enough a lot of it was just going straight through and not trickling down, it was being wasted. I had the pressure cut back and I think I settled on 60 pounds when most of the water was actually going onto the fire.

'When my deputy, Tom Hughes, came back in to work the pair of us went up to have a look at things from the roof of the reactor. The water wasn't really showing any particular extinguishing effect. It was having some cooling effect, because we were producing steam. As there was nobody on the charge hoist now we didn't need ventilation there. As we'd got an alternative coolant, in the water, we didn't need to keep air going through to cool the surrounding graphite. So we decided to shut off all the air.

'When I had the shutdown fans turned off I went back up to the roof again. I had one hell of a job to lever the discs off the inspection holes at the back. The fire, not now being fed with air, was trying to get air from wherever it could. There wasn't a rush of flames, as it was now almost certainly pulling air down through the chimney. It was dramatic. I could see the fire dying out. I could see the flames receding and by about twelve o'clock I could see nothing. As far as I was concerned the fire was out, but we kept the water going for another twenty-four hours. Then we had a mess, because the water, which was radioactive now, was coming out all over the place. It flooded two forecourts. We really had a bit of a mess on our hands to clean up. The filters that were at the top of the chimney were very radioactive, particularly with radioactive iodine and certainly strontium.

'What happened at Chernobyl was a very different proposition, because that just went off, pop! The sort of situation that I and the men on the charge hoist were facing was tackling the fire throughout the night. It was a meltdown, if you've got burning metal then the stuff's melting. The fire never spread beyond the original 140 channels, although it spread along the channels.

'This situation hadn't been envisaged. That's why we had no provisions for dealing with it. We had to improvise and our improvisation was brilliant. In fact I think we got a pat on the back from the Board of Inquiry under Sir William Penney. Quite a night. I'm glad I was there, but I'd rather not do it again.'

The full version of the official report on the accident was eventually released in January 1988 under the Official Secrets thirty-year rule. It claimed that the heat build up went too far as the thermocouples were in the wrong place to measure the points of highest temperature. But, as Arthur Wilson has lived to testify, he and others had put the thermocouples in the places designated, so it really was a design fault.

There are many who believe that the likes of Touhy and others who fought the fire should have got far more recognition for what they did. In 1964 Touhy was promoted to Managing Director of all the UKAEA plants, but this was because he was well due for promotion. In the Soviet Union firefighters and others involved with Chernobyl were publicly presented with medals and fêted like heroes. But in order to play down the significance of the event, and to suppress public interest in our nuclear-bomb factory, the men on site had to be content with a 'pat on the back'.

Like their Soviet counterparts the Windscale men were exposed to radiation whilst dealing with the fire. Touhy does not know how much radiation he received that night. 'Why it happened I don't know, but for the latter part of the night when it was getting worse and worse on the charge hoist I didn't have monitoring equipment on me. I think unconsciously the reason I didn't have things on me I was just a bit afraid somebody would come along and say, "Look, you've had too much" and I knew I had to be there. They did estimates and I think they reckoned I got about four years' maximum exposure as it was then.'

However, Tom Touhy's experience has convinced him that radiation is much less dangerous than we think. 'It just shows you can have a lot more radiation than is being said, without it having any real adverse effect. They've been paying out compensation on really very moderate doses of radiation which in my opinion is ridiculous. I'm walking proof, a pretty good physical specimen to be in my seventy-second year, radiation or no radiation. There is absolutely no justification for the fuss being made about leukaemias or anything else. To some extent it serves the present management right for getting themselves into this stupid position by giving compensation when compensation was never justified. If you do that once then you're on the slippery slope.'

Not all those present at the fire were as calm as Arthur and Tom. Jack Coyle told me how he felt after that night. 'I was at Sellafield from 1951 until 1980. I was a maintenance fitter and when the fire went up I was asked to stay on site. I didn't want to, I can't say why. I hadn't really thought about the danger up till then, it was like the war really, until you got to the front I don't suppose you really thought about it. The worst moment was when they put the water on to dowse the fire. I remember I wanted to run, I really felt scared, but you'd never admit as much to anyone. All the scientists I'd seen that day looking really worried, not their usual cocky selves. One lad standing next to me said, "We should open a book on it, you know." He meant have a bet. I thought to myself I'd win a bloody race if it was out of this place. I asked someone if they thought it would take long as I wanted to get home. He said, "You daft bugger, we all want to get home, but they'll not be letting us go if this goes wrong. We'll be lepers if we go home covered in this stuff." For some of the men it almost seemed exciting. I read about those men who came from Capenhurst to help fight the fire. God, they must have been mad. After helping clear away some of the safety equipment we were allowed to go. I wanted to walk back home, I felt strained. On my way up our street I just stopped walking. I just thought, my God, I might never have seen home again. After that, well, I can't tell the strain it's put on me. I suppose most of the time I just buried it. I hated the place, but what else could I do? I felt particularly bad when they agreed to those Japanese imports. I wondered then what all the bloody sacrifice had been for during the war.'

Jack was not the only person concerned about the people outside. As Tom Touhy explained, the workers thought the public was being taken care of. 'The health physics people of the time first detected that there was some trouble with the reactor by having picked up high readings in atmospheric samples. After the fire people felt pleased with themselves because the first milk samples were negative. But twenty-four hours later the radioactive iodine began to come through and so they had to impose a milk ban.'

As Touhy was the works manager at the time, he admits he did not know exactly what was happening over the perimeter fence.

'Quite honestly I can't answer if the public was warned at the time. I was involved with fighting the fire and I was only interested in getting the bloody fire out. I was living nearby at the time and before I left home I made sure all the windows were shut. I knew that there'd be a certain amount of airborne activity, but I knew the filters were darn good too.'

Touhy's confidence was not entirely justified. Local farmer Tyson Dawson recalled: 'We had two sisters who both had babies at the time. During the Friday they were parked outside, right next to the factory fence. One was just four months old and one was eighteen months. The wind was coming from the west and it was drifting our way. Actually we felt rather odd at the time of the fire because our house was probably 200 yards from where the factory was, right up against the factory fence and the following morning, this occurred on the Thursday, on the Friday morning we were looking down on the works and everybody was going home at 10.30 a.m. and we were wondering why. We were quite annoyed when we found out because it was enough for the workers the other side of the fence to go home and we had these young babies. Fortunately they've never suffered any ill effects. We never got to know until through the night on Saturday about two o'clock on Sunday morning. A knock came on the door. Of course I got up to see who it was. It was the local policeman with an official from the works. We hadn't to drink any more of our milk, we had to take other precautions. It was a very serious thing if we drank milk. At the time of the fire itself they didn't seem to have a great deal of information, but one of the things they stressed was we hadn't to eat any of the vegetables that were grown on the farm, but particularly the milk. Of course we didn't really believe this. I was quite annoyed because we had gone almost three days before they had informed us there was anything seriously wrong with the works.'

'People were worried at the time of the fire. We had a big meeting with farmers at Gosforth a week after the fire. It was rather funny because they all came to have it explained by the Sellafield officials, what had happened and why. The local people living round weren't the least bit concerned, but all the ones from round Kirksanton and Whicham Valley – they were most concerned, terrified almost, frightened to death. I knew these people.

When I met them at this public hall I said, "Why are you so afraid?" and they said, "This is going to be terrible." I asked them how they would like to live against it, at the fence, right against it, if your house is only ten yards away. They said they'd move away. It's funny how they were worried even though they were from further away.'

Some of the workers themselves were not fully informed. Val Hampshire was eighteen when the accident took place. She was working on the first trigger for nuclear weapons, Polonium-210. A canister of this was in the Pile at the time of the fire and was released over the surrounding countryside. Val remembers, 'I wasn't aware that I was working with polonium. It was so sensitive it had a code name at the time which wasn't its element code. It was always known as LM, so that is why I never made the connection. I didn't know the connection between that and the bomb trigger until after I had left. That there was polonium at the bottom of the pile which was released during the fire was something that I didn't know at the time.'

Polonium-210 is one of the most toxic substances known to man, far more toxic even than plutonium. 'We were all so young. To us the fire was an exciting thing. The day it happened we weren't told. The day after a lot of us were sent out with a driver to the local farmers to tell them to destroy their milk, to pour it away. I had to have somebody else with me because this must have sounded a bit barmy coming from an eighteen year old. Of course communication wasn't that good anyway, some of these farms were very remote. I didn't feel threatened at all, but obviously my brother-in-law did. He stopped his children drinking local milk and bought in evaporated milk, and that's what they had for years. He was a scientist at the Freshwater Biological Institute. He placed a core sample at the bottom of one of the lakes in order to test for the Cs-137 fallout.' At the time Val was married to Judd Weldon, who was the site photographer. The camera he used to try to take photographs inside the reactor building after the fire was sent to Drigg. None of the photographs ever came out because the radiation had clouded the film. Judd died of leukaemia in 1984.

The local police were so worried about the outcome of the fire that they had emergency rolling stock drawn into Whitehaven rail yard in order to evacuate people. In the end all that happened was that some research was done from 1958 to 1962 on the health of Cumbrian people. This information is still kept secret under the thirty-year rule.

However, some work on the health effects of the fire did eventually emerge. In 1982 the Political Ecology Research Group (PERG), an Oxford-based science group, issued their estimates of the numbers affected by the 1957 fire. They have discovered that the accident had released 100–1,000 times more radioactive Iodine-131 than the Three Mile Island Accident in America in 1979. The cloud had passed over England into Holland and Germany and finally southern Scandanavia. PERG concluded some 250 thyroid cancers had been caused, some 13 to 30 of which would be fatal. In February 1983 the National Radiological Protection Board published their first report on the fire, in which they agreed with PERG's report. The NRPB were at pains to point out these were hypothetical deaths.

The head of health physics for the United Kingdom Atomic Energy Authority at the time of the fire was Dr John Dunster. He had measured the polonium levels in the area around Windscale after the accident and published the results. However, when the NRPB published their report on the fire they failed to take into account the polonium, even though by this time Dunster was their director. An estimate of the possible effects of the polonium was published when John Urquhart, a statistician from Newcastle University, unearthed Dunster's early monitoring results. Urquhart also had a copy of a report which the NRPB had done on the effects of Polonium-210 from coal-powered plants. Using the NRPB estimates for the uptake of polonium in meat and milk given in the report on coal, Urquhart calculated the 240 curies of polonium released from the fire would cause 1,000 cancer deaths. The NRPB then back-tracked. They dismissed figures used in their own assessment from coal-powered stations. They also attacked the methods used to measure polonium in 1957 and said that there would be 'inconsistencies'. They eventually issued a report saying that the polonium release would have caused, possibly, an extra twelve deaths.

One of the authors of the original NRPB report on the fire, Dr Linsley, said that those living near Windscale at the time of the fire would be twice as likely to contract thyroid cancer due to the fallout, with children most likely to be effected. The risk of their developing thyroid cancer during their lives as a result of the accident is one in a thousand (e/m 18/2/83). In 1984 Professor Fremlin, Cumbria County Council's radiation advisor, suggested that an *ex gratia* payment should be paid by the Government to anyone who contracted thyroid cancer in the Windscale area within twenty years of the fire. It is not possible to prove beyond doubt that any cancer is actually caused by natural or man-made radioactivity. No member of the public has, as yet, sued BNFL because of thyroid cancer.

Unfortunately for Alix Bryson her thyroid cancer manifested itself twenty-one years after the fire, a year too late for Fremlin's advice. She was at school nearby the plant when the fire happened. 'I do recall a little bit of panic and some of the parents came in the night and took their children away, but there was no feeling that there was anything to really worry about.' In 1979 Alix found she had a lymphoma of the thyroid gland. 'It was about a year after that when there were reports about TMI nuclear accident and I read a report that it wasn't nearly as bad as the Windscale Fire in 1957. I was stunned. That's when I first thought about the connection. Now there is no doubt in my mind that there is a link.' Alix had her thyroid removed and underwent extensive medical treatment. 'It was a very frightening experience, a terrible time, and I want other women who were at my school in 1957 to go and get check-ups now so that it will be discovered early enough. When I tried to get some sense out of the authorities they wouldn't admit to any link at all. They won't accept the responsibility, although this type of cancer occurs only through exposure to radiation.'

CHAPTER

2

*The condition upon which God hath given man liberty is eternal
vigilance; which condition if he break, servitude is at once the
consequence of his crime, and the punishment of his guilt.*
Speech 1790, John Philpot Curran

The now-defunct Plutonium Piles were just the beginning of the
huge Sellafield complex. The Sellafield site, originally owned by
the Ministry of Supply, was handed over to the United Kingdom
Atomic Energy Authority when it was formed in 1956. In turn the
UKAEA passed over the running of the site when British Nuclear
Fuels was formed in 1971. BNFL is to all intents and purposes a
private company, with its shares owned by the Secretary of State
for Energy on behalf of the taxpayer.

The main section of Sellafield is the Windscale reprocessing
plant. In fact it is the reprocessing operation which distinguishes
Sellafield as a nuclear establishment. Reprocessing is quite easy to
understand. Hot spent nuclear fuel, which has been partially burnt
in a nuclear reactor, is taken to the B205 reprocessing building at
Windscale and chemically separated into its three main constituents. These are uranium, plutonium and nuclear waste.

The uranium taken out during this process is not as good as raw
uranium for burning, but it can be used again if some fresh uranium is injected into it. This reprocessed uranium is like the
cinders left after a coal fire. The plutonium can be used either for
weapons or for fuel in a fast-breeder reactor. However the major
drawback with reprocessing is that at every stage it creates nuclear
wastes in many different forms. These range from solid low-level
waste like contaminated tools and machinery, the marine discharges into the Irish Sea and the high-level nuclear waste which is
kept in silos. Reprocessing also accounts for the largest amount of
radioactive discharges in the whole nuclear fuel cycle and for the
majority of worker and public radiation doses.

The Windscale section contains the plutonium laboratories; the nuclear-waste treatment plants; the old reprocessing plant B204 (closed after a serious accident in 1973), the intermediate and high-level waste silos, research and development labs and fuel storage ponds. The UKAEA also has some research buildings on the site as well as the experimental advanced gas-cooled reactor (AGR).

The other half of Sellafield is the four Calder Hall magnox reactors which lie just to the south of the Calder River. The word magnox is taken from the type of fuel burnt in this sort of plant. Opened in 1956, the reactors were the first large scale nuclear plants in the world which were meant to provide 'electricity too cheap to meter'. The reasoning behind this hackneyed phrase was not well known in the 1950s, but we now know that these reactors were an extension of the nuclear weapons programme and the electricity they produced was a by-product. The Calder plants are classed as military reactors because they can supply plutonium for nuclear bombs without breaking the international conventions which restrict the sale and use of plutonium taken from civilian reactors.

Piya Guneratne has worked on several of the facilities within Sellafield. He started at Sellafield in 1952 and finished in 1984. Born in Sri Lanka in 1919, Piya came to England in 1937 and studied at University College London, where he gained an honours degree and diploma in electrical engineering.

'I joined the United Kingdom Atomic Energy Authority Research and Development Department in 1952. I was very enthusiastic about joining the industry because it was a new field. Initially I was on heat transfer and at that time I was also doing heat-transfer experiments on the Windscale Pile Number One. During my early days I took out several patents, on methods of temperature measurement and development of thermocoupling techniques. All of these patents have been signed over to the authority and some have been used with success.'

Piya and his wife now live in Millom, but at the time of the 1957 fire they and their three children lived in Seascale. 'I was not on site when the Pile caught fire. I did not know about it until a colleague of mine met me in the street and told me about it. By the time I got home my wife had also heard about the fire from a neighbour who had been round and warned her to take the

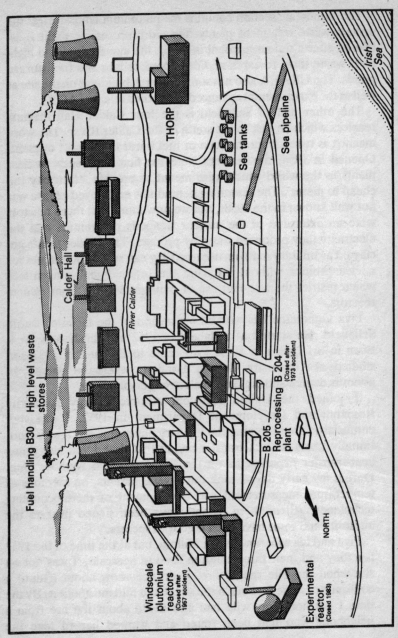

Artist's Impression of the Sellafield Site

Irish Sea

Sea pipeline

Sea tanks

THORP

Calder Hall

River Calder

High level waste stores

Fuel handling B30

B 204
(Closed after
1973 accident)

Reprocessing
plant

B 205

NORTH

Windscale plutonium reactors
(Closed after
1967 accident)

Experimental
reactor
(Closed 1983)

children in from the garden. When I came home my wife was very concerned. We decided immediately to take the children away from Seascale. We motored down to South Wales where I left my wife and children. I returned almost immediately to be at work the following day. After I came back I took my daughter's shoes into the laboratory to check the radioactivity levels as she had been in the garden at the time of the fire. The radioactivity levels found on her shoes were found to be very much higher than on my own shoes.

'I felt no sense of danger about a fire in the reactor. I thought that it would be put out soon and that it was just an overheating of a few channels. The impact of the fire did not quite register on me at the time because I thought the fire could not have been all that serious. I had no idea of what the safe levels were, but when my daughter's shoes were monitored I felt I had done the right thing in taking the children away from Seascale.'

Piya, like Arthur Wilson, had gone into the bottom of the reactor chimney to push irradiated fuel into the cooling ponds. It is an experience Piya cannot forget. 'During other shutdowns on the reactors, prior to 1957, I had been inside the air duct pushing irradiated fuel elements into the water. At the time I wore a Windscale suit, which had its own air supply. Going into the air duct the first time was a very frightening experience. It was like going into a huge, dark dungeon not knowing what was in front of you. I had looked at the drawings before I went in to make sure I did not overstep my mark and fall into the water duct. I was asked to push these fuel elements into a water duct with a squeegy at the end of a long pole. I had a pole, pushing fuel elements about eight feet away, but there may have been others, about a couple of feet away. I may have knocked one of them with my foot as I went past. I never knew how close I was to the fuel elements. I think it was something I did not appreciate the dangers of at the time which would not be allowed today by law. These fuel rods are very radioactive, contact with them can lead to death in a very short time.

'When I had first started at Windscale I expected instruction and training to be given on radiological hazards, but that was never the case. We were thrown in at the deep end. Even my superiors did not know very much about radiation. When it was announced that they would be taking the Piles down they said that they would be designing robots to do the work. This is after thirty years when quite an amount of the radioactivity has decayed. In the early days we actually went in there! The second entry into the chimney base for removing fuel elements resulted in my getting an overdose and I was told then that I could not be used for that type of work again, as I had exceeded my dose.

'After the fire I was asked to help investigate the cause, because I had conducted experiments in Pile Number One on temperatures in nuclear fuel. My laboratory managers asked me to conduct an experiment with a mock graphite stack, with lithium cartridges, to see if there was any possibility of it catching fire with an electrically heated graphite core. The result was negative, which was not unexpected, because we could not get the amount of heat required by electrical heating that you would get in a nuclear reaction. The fact is that the change and expansion caused by a nuclear reaction near to graphite cannot occur after simple electrical heating. Although I was involved in experiments on the reactor and even though my expertise was in thermocouples and temperature readings I was never asked to give evidence to the official inquiry into the cause of the fire. The experiments I was asked to do with the mock graphite stack showed that the managers did not understand the situation. One man who has voiced concern over the fire and, who sent a letter of complaint to the Prime Minister, Macmillan, was Frank Lesley. He was called "a self-opinionated ass" by the UKAEA. He would ask embarrassing questions at safety meetings. He was a very good scientist, but like most people who spoke out, who questioned the work practices, he was not liked.'

Despite the accident Piya went on to undertake experiments involving the radiation testing of typical civil reactor fuel elements in both Calder Hall and Chapel Cross reactors. This work was equally distributed between Calder Hall and Chapel Cross for eight years and then Piya transferred most of his work to the advanced gas-cooled reactor where he was involved with troubleshooting on thermocouple failures and the development of temperature measuring techniques.

Being a methodical man Piya determined to keep his health in check after he retired in 1984 and so arranged for an examination with his own GP. 'I went to my GP at the end of 1984 and asked him for a test, which found nothing. The following year, in 1985, they found that one of the lymph glands in my neck was swollen. They referred me to Whitehaven Hospital and had me admitted the following day for tests. I was discharged from hospital with the suggestion there was pancreatic cancer for which there is no treatment. I had approximately three months to live. I was asked by the consultant to try to resign myself to this fact and take up religious thoughts and try to come to terms with the remainder of my life. In my bones I felt he was quite wrong because I had no pains, which he said I should have, at that time. The first action I took was to summon my solicitor to make my will.

'I was gradually getting weaker and weaker at this time. I was losing weight and could hardly walk. Luckily my daughter in Leeds had me admitted to Leeds Hospital from where I was immediately transferred to the Bradford Royal Infirmary, under a specialist in cancer. The results of his tests confirmed I had non-Hodgkin's lymphoma, for which there is a cure. I was so weak that when I left I was taken from the house on a stretcher to the ambulance, but I was able to walk back into my home.

'It is difficult to say how long I had the cancer before it manifested itself, but my consultant tells me that I must have had it for seven or eight years before it was detected. I had annual medical examinations at Windscale, but they had not spotted it at the time, which I am very surprised at. The radiation exposure that caused my cancer obviously came from the dose that I received whilst I was at Windscale. Although the doses initially do not appear to be very high compared to the limit which is currently accepted, I have my grave doubts about the measurements taken in the 1950s. I am not satisfied that all the doses I have had in the nuclear industry have been recorded. I am worried because whilst I worked at Chapel Cross I received a radiation dose, both the records for this and my second entry into the pile air ducts are missing. I believe that for some doses you could multiply the amount five or six times to get the true figures. I also had to write and ask for my dose records when I retired, when they should just have been sent. I have had no word from anybody at Sellafield. During my time in the Whitehaven Hospital one of my colleagues called in to see me as he had heard that I was in hospital. Nobody else, although they knew that I was in hospital, came to see me.

Either they were afraid to come and see or they were far too embarrassed to come, I just don't know the reason for this.

'A friend of mine whom I knew from our very early training days at Sellafield died of cancer, about two or three years before I contracted the disease. I do feel I am one of the lucky ones. I am one of the people who got away. Otherwise today you would just be interviewing my widow.'

The need for men to go into the air ducts of the Plutonium Piles to push fuel into the cooling ponds, as described by Piya Guneratne, was a direct result of the improvised methods used to operate the Piles. As Tom Touhy explained, the fuel was discharged by being pushed out of the end of the channels in which it rested. Beyond those channels, at the back of the reactor, were two enormous ducts at the base of the chimney, through which the air escaped. 'Some of the fuel channels were opposite these ducts so there was some risk, in discharging fuel, that you would shoot some of the fuel elements over into the base of the chimney. Now, this was recognised during the design of the reactor and a number of baffles were put in these outlet air ducts.'

The baffles, however, were removed when it was found they were decreasing the efficiency of the reactor. The original charge machine had been designed to move the fuel rods so they would fall into the water. But because the men improvised with drain rods there was no control over the amount of push. It was found that 'fuel elements were accumulating in the base of the outlet air ducts having been too forcibly pushed.'

But that was not the end of the problem, as Tom explained. 'Because some of the fuel rods had come from higher up the reactor the bigger the bang when they hit the floor of the duct. Of course the protective can around the fuel rod could split and here these things were oxidising away quite nicely in the outlet air ducts without anybody knowing about it. This gave rise to the Strontium-90 releases. Most of it was obviously trapped on the filter, because it was in particulate form, but some of it got out into the fields immediately around Windscale. It didn't get out very far afield, but some got into the milk.'

Although Touhy believed that the strontium did not get very far a government report, released under the thirty-year rule in January 1989, showed that 800 farms were contaminated by the releases!

One of those who had the misfortune to be living right next to the plant at the time was Walker Bateman. Dorothy, his wife, believes she is lucky that she did not join Walker on the family farm until 1958 when these releases had ended. The Batemens are friendly and trusting and are very much of the old breed of people brought up on the west coast, except in one respect – they mistrust and dislike the nuclear industry. Not that they have always held this view.

Walker and Dorothy lived next to the plant for twenty-six years. Walker's family have owned and farmed the Yottenfews holding, now part of Sellafield, for 300 years. Walker's uncle Isaac owned the very farm called Sellafield on which the plant is built. 'His house was where the new canteen is now,' Walker recalls. Dorothy and Walker have watched the plant grow. 'I can remember when there was no factory, not even the TNT plant, on the land. Then they built that. When the Queen opened Calder Hall Dorothy and I were courting. We went along to watch the opening. We thought it was exciting. We were told the electricity would be too cheap to meter. We had no idea in those days what it was all about, we were never really aware of the military aspects of the plant, not in the early years. We simply assumed that the Plutonium Piles, which towered over the skyline outside our house, were for electricity.'

The house Walker speaks of is one of the cottages belonging to Yottenfews farm. Their house is the last before the plant begins at the North Gate. Over the years Walker had had to stand by as his family's farm was slowly enveloped by Sellafield, piece by piece, and they were forced to sell land to the company. 'My father was dead against the plant, he tried to prevent them taking the land. He appreciated the value of land and he realised once industry had got it it would never be the same again. We used to have a piece of woodland on the Beckermet road. Every time the hounds were hunting in Ladywood the deer would come across the river and hide in our little wood. The next morning if you crept round you would see them. Then they put the road down for THORP, the Thermal Oxide Reprocessing Plant and the car park. The result was the deer would cross the river and because they weren't able to find the wood they would run up and down the road. It was sad to see. There were also rare spotted orchids in that land: they went. And the frogs, they had a pond and you'd hear them shouting. Now they've gone too.' BNFL bought the last piece of land in 1987.

But even by the mid-fifties the farm had become too small to support all those living on it and so Walker had to take work at Sellafield. 'I started work there in 1958 when I got married. The thing was I had to have work and there was nothing else in the area. I had no trade so there was absolutely nothing else but the factory at the time. I don't think I was thrilled, but it was a new opening for me and it was just one of those things you've got to make the best of.'

Looking back Dorothy remembers with anger and bitterness how the authorities kept them in the dark over the accidental releases. 'We didn't realise it was dangerous, we were never told any of the dangers that existed. They never told us a thing. I'm afraid we took our three children down on the beach when they were smaller. Thankfully we didn't use the beach a lot as we had a big garden and our own paddling pool, although we did enjoy walks along the beach. We were ignorant and so was everybody else. It was only when we started reading and asking questions that we learnt the dangers we'd been exposed to. We realise now that nobody protected us. We lived all those years next to the plant and they never once came to monitor the garden, we grew and ate our own vegetables and fruit. But we've never been checked and nobody had ever come to ask us anything. We were very naïve and trusting. But we weren't being protected by anybody, not the NRPB, not the Government, not Copeland Environmental Health – nobody.'

Of course, not everyone shares Walker and Dorothy's view. Tony Hildrop is now retired, but he worked at Sellafield for almost thirty years. He's one of the County Councillors for the Copeland area and is Chairman of Cumbria Tourist Board. He started work there as a joiner during Calder Hall's construction and went on to work for the UKAEA, in reprocessing, from 1959. He was born in Byker, in the North East, sixty-three years ago. 'My experience of the industry has been a good one. At the beginning there was camaraderie which was hard to get in the normal work that I was used to. It was worth a couple of quid a week just working there!'

For Tony Hildrop working on nuclear power was a real bonus. 'I'm a science-fiction fan. I remember as a youngster, my father catching me reading this book which concerned men working in a nuclear reactor and the stresses and strains that the staff were going under. He asked me what I was reading that for, it's nonsense, it'll never happen. I always remember that book because it was before the war and I was only a youngster. What would my father think now? I fulfilled a sort of childhood fantasy. My father had vision, he was an idealist much more than anything else, but he still couldn't see that view that science would allow us to do certain things. I'm not an idealist, but I don't believe the nuclear-waste problem is insurmountable. I believe that in future the waste can be treated. If you don't believe anything like that you don't believe there's any future for the industrial processes in this world. If you don't move forward you're dead.'

The enthusiasm of men like Hildrop was to prove a great support to the nuclear industry as it went through many difficulties. However, like many others, Tony is not 100 per cent behind everything done on-site. The military connection with nuclear power does concern him. Hildrop recalled, 'I don't support atomic weapons in any shape or form. I brook no argument on that. Originally the Calder Hall reactors were used for the production of plutonium for military uses, something I totally oppose. Now electrical production provides the driving force. They are good reactors and have been described as work horses. I believe that there are far more good and far more useful uses for nuclear energy.

'There's so much misunderstanding about the whole industry, but it's still not as open as it should be because of its military background. I'm not alone in that 80 to 90 per cent of the people who work in the industry are totally opposed to nuclear weapons. Because we are closer to the problem than most people we can see the damage that can be done by nuclear power. People who work on the site have got a much clearer understanding of what nuclear weapons are than a lot of people who do a lot of shouting about it. We are dealing with it on a day-to-day basis, we know that if we disregard the safety aspects we're going to end up in trouble.'

Hildrop was one of a breed of young men who had seen hard times prior to the war. Nuclear power was seen by many as part of the golden post-war era. These people were not to be deterred by the unknown risks of the industry, nor by any rumours of the harm radiation could do. The area had suffered its own loss of life with the coal industry. In 1946 Whitehaven was deeply shocked when 104 men had died in an accident in William Pit in Egremont. The area was also rife with tuberculosis. My mother told me that one of my uncles, born and raised in Cleator Moor, lost six brothers and sisters from a family of thirteen children. They all died of TB. For most people the call to go through Sellafield's gates was purely practical. Many had seen the writing on the wall some time before. These people believed that Sellafield might be their last chance. Had not one of the most influential post-war thinkers said as much? The *Whitehaven News* carried the following report in September 1947 under the heading 'Let Those Towns Die'.

Professor Joad, a member of the Government's post-war think tank, said:

> I make a serious proposal. The towns of West Cumberland, during much of my lifetime of fifty-six years, have suffered from unemployment. Their utility went when the mines gave out or partly gave out, and there have been continuous, artificial attempts at restoration through development grants and subsidies ending in Government's substitution of an atomic power experimental plant for the Courtaulds factory at Sellafield. Why? Because we must find work for the people to come in. Why not let these towns die? Why not redistribute the population centres where manpower is desperately needed? The present generation will object to this proposal, but the younger generation would be eternally grateful in not being brought up in such deadends. Meanwhile the Lake District would not be menaced by the demands for new roads and sites, and atomic power stations. Surely the atomic plant now going up on the south-west Cumberland coast is the "halt" signal.

Most people reading Joad's words will find them prophetic. But they can hardly have been comforting to locals of the time. For many of the blue-collar workers there was an opportunity to move up the ladder, learn new skills and become adept in an industry that everyone was new to. One such man was Stewart Tyler.

He came out of the Coldstream Guards back to the bleak industrial landscape of Cumbria. He started at Sellafield in 1948, the very earliest days of the weapons project. His widow, Dorothy (Dolly) Tyler, lives in a terraced house in Frizington, a small village set around the nearby opencast coal-mine. Frizington is almost as dire a place as the mine itself, with the distant hills providing the only saving grace. Dolly is a hardy character with the sort of accent you could cut with a knife. Her husband, Stewart Tyler, died aged fifty-three in 1976.

When Mr Tyler died at the hospital in Newcastle, no post-mortem was carried out. The death certificate states he died of a stomach cancer. There was never an examination of the internal organs. It would have been important to establish the site of the cancer as, if it had been started in the pancreas, it would be more likely to be radiation linked.

When CORE took up the case we first approached Tyler's union, the General Municipal and Boilermakers (GMB). They looked at the dose record, which Mrs Tyler has still not seen, and said that under the present scheme her claim would probably not hold.

Dolly remembers how hard her husband's working life was: 'Before Sellafield Stew had been in the pits. When William Pit went up he was there. I remember him coming home and saying how terrible it was when they were bringing men to the surface. He worked on Sellafield security for eighteen months and after security he went into the reprocessing area. Now and again he'd be put out of the radioactive area because he'd been contaminated. Many's the time he used to come home and he'd have all sorts of different clothes on. He'd have stripped right through to his under-pants and vest and shoes and socks – the lot. He'd get stuck on cutting the grass at Sellafield and would have his wages docked. He enjoyed good health though, with only a few weeks off because he slipped a disc. He saw it as quite a clean industry after being in the pits, but the wages weren't very good. He said you couldn't expect much because they weren't doing much – not compared to the labour they had in the pits. He thought it was a clean area and that it was all right, but then it changed. After 1956 he said if we went on any more trips, to the seaside, he'd be dead against them. He said, 'I'll take my lad on no more bloody trips to the beach'. He used to say, 'If you're going anywhere don't go down, go up, keep away from the bloody spot', but that was all he ever said. He used to warn me about this, that and the other. I thought he was mad because I didn't hear any news about it. He came home about three hours late because of the '57 fire. Again he wouldn't talk about it. It wasn't until years later I learnt how serious it was.

Anyway, he went off fish, he wouldn't have it. When the gas reactor was built he said he didn't like that either.'

The 'area' is where the main reprocessing operations take place and it is this part of the site which is the most contaminated. If Stewart Tyler was so badly contaminated that he had to throw away his own clothing then he was probably scrubbed also to remove contamination from his body, a process which can be quite horrendous. If someone gets badly contaminated the part of their body that came into contact with radioactive material is scrubbed, sometimes until it bleeds. The inside of the ears and nose are cleaned out. Eyes get mild washes of medical fluids. Mouthwashes are also given. The hair can be cut out and the scalp scrubbed. The finger nails are scrubbed, cut down and, occasionally, the finger-nail layers pared down. If the contamination involves a cut the skin surrounding the puncture is cut away. Such people should have a close eye kept on them for health effects. Dorothy Tyler continues: 'Stew had cancer, but he used to come in and say he'd had a medical, but they never found anything. Surely they were bound to notice something? He said he was passing blood, then his stomach took bad. He was still working for BNFL at the time. His bowels were so bad we had to move from the set of terraced houses we lived in because we shared communal toilets in the backyard. He said he was embarrassed. Stew was going a dirty yellow colour. I knew he had cancer. You know if you live with a person – you can tell the change. He'd been taken into hospital on 11th April and was dead by 11th May.

'Although he was a shop steward he never saw the unions in hospital. Stew told me that if ever anything went wrong I was to contact them. I rang a union man who told me there was nothing to worry about, he said the pond area is not even "active". I thought he would know these things because he worked there. Now I know my husband worked in the area for twenty years, in some of the most radioactive parts. All but one of the men Stew worked with are dead.'

At the time Stewart Tyler died there was no compensation scheme for Dolly to apply to. There was no way she could have afforded to take the case forward herself. When in 1980, the compensation scheme was first mooted, she was approached by a union representative and asked if she would like to have a claim put in on her behalf and she agreed to this. She says that he told her not to hold out too much hope as cancer was hereditary! Apart from the fact that this is absolute nonsense none of Tyler's relatives had died with it. Dolly hopes to have her case reviewed in the near future.

Dolly feels a sense of bitterness at what unthinking industrial expansion has done to the area she was born in. 'I've lived in the area all my life and I really love it. I have thought about what industry has done to the area. I was going to bingo the other night. I was sitting on the bus and on one side there was Keekle, the opencast mine. I thought, they are pulling the guts out of this area on one side, and poisoning it on the other. Now they are fetching a pile of German nuclear waste in. It's sickening. I don't think Sellafield has done a thing for the workers in this area. All it's done is got them into debt. They can't do anything else now, only work there. They've shut the steelworks, the coal mines. It's as if they've cleaned out all the other industry so that everybody has to go to work there. They think we are sheep shaggers in this area – and we must be to let them get away with it.'

Mr J. Wilson of Seascale died aged sixty-four of a thyroid cancer in 1984. Mr Wilson worked at Sellafield for thirty-two years, retiring because of ill health in 1983. At his inquest the jury was told Mr Wilson was employed in the separation plant as a process worker. He was a non-smoker who rarely took a drink. His hobbies were sea-fishing, bird-watching and reading. He had been fit and active up to two years before his death, when he started to complain of backache. In September 1983 he had a lump removed from his neck. The growth was found to be malignant.

Mrs Wilson explained to the coroner that she remembered one incident in particular relating to contamination. In 1973 her husband had come home from night shift very worried. His face was red and his skin broken. He told her that he had been involved in a small incident and that was how he had come to be contaminated. The medical people had scrubbed his face, ears, nose and head to remove the contamination. Apparently he and another man had been walking through part of the plant when the other man had tapped a hose pipe; this resulted in a shower of what must have been contaminated dust falling on Mr Wilson's head. Mrs Wilson said that her husband had been contaminated on several other occasions and that this had been picked up when other checks had been made.

The evidence of the works medical people said Mr Wilson had been accepted by the company as a Category One employee on 13th February 1951. He immediately started work in the separation area, where radiation badges had to be worn as 'there was a potential for exposure'. Mr Wilson had taken part in a medical survey in 1967 and his thyroid was found to be enlarged, but subsequent checks had shown no deterioration or cause for concern. BNFL confirmed that Wilson had suffered skin contamination on several occasions. In 1973 he had suffered nasal contamination, a result of the accident Mrs Wilson remembered. Because of this Mr Wilson had been put 'outside the area' for a fortnight.

Could Mr Wilson's thyroid cancer have been treated earlier? Dr Barrie Walker, one of the local Seascale GPs, wrote an article in which he bemoaned the fact that he could be dealing with someone who had been contaminated, but he would not know this as the company never wrote to tell him. Walker said the company was not liaising enough with the GPs of workers. One of BNFL's medical officers wrote back saying, 'If I had to write and tell local GPs every time a worker was contaminated I'd be writing a hundred letters a day'. Walker was worried because a third of his list of 2,000 patients are Sellafield workers. Walker had seen one man who complained of having a burning sensation in his neck and face. 'Later he was diagnosed as having a thyroid cancer. It transpired after his death that he had received an overexposure at work and had to have his skin scrubbed. I am still not aware of his actual exposure.' Dr Walker believes that if he had known early enough of the worker's exposure he might have been able to treat the patient and catch the cancer in time. Walker also noted that this was not an isolated case (obs 10.8.86). I suspect that the unnamed worker was Mr Wilson.

One of the saddest cases CORE has ever dealt with regarding a Sellafield worker was that of Gary White. We were contacted by Gary's brother, Ken, in April of 1986. Gary, then twenty-six, had been diagnosed as having cancer of the perotid gland. At the time Gary was working on the dismantling of the advanced gas-cooled reactor. Ken believed his brother's cancer was due to working at

Sellafield and he wanted our help. Gary lived on the large council estate just east of Whitehaven. The Marchon detergent factory across the smoke-filled valley below, notorious in West Cumbria for its leaks and discharges, made Sellafield seem like a clean place to work in. Gary and Ken had done a number of construction jobs, both inside and outside the active area, on the site. When Gary got a job with the UKAEA on the first decommissioning of a British reactor, the AGR, it seemed a good prospect as the job might have led on to better things. Better to work for the establishment than a construction firm. Gary and his colleagues did most of the heavy work. They would remove various parts of the peripheral reactor equipment whilst other workers, in protective clothing, would go into the 'hotter' areas. As Gary told me sometimes he would be working, unprotected, in an area a few yards from people in the full Windscale suit. As usual orange bunting would be strung between the two sets of workers.

Gary told me he had been involved in one or two radiation incidents. On one occasion he remembers the whole of the building, offices and all, being contaminated through a release of radioactive contaminated material from the reactor. Gary said that he and the other lads got a fortnight's overtime on the clean-up operation. He could not give us exact information on what had happened. Like most workers he did not think he would ever need to record in detail the experiences of his work. Another time he was contaminated and he was told that he had a very high radioactive reading from a nose swab that was taken. Once again he did not have the details. He hoped we could get them for him. During the conversation he told us that not only did he have a cancerous gland, but that he had also been diagnosed as having a lung cancer. There is no cure for this.

Gary had begun to feel ill in October 1986. Like many on site he opted to visit the BNFL surgery rather than go to his own GP. For three months he tried to get an appointment with one of the doctors, but only ever got to see the nurses. He was told that his lump was no more than an irritated gland and that if he ate a boiled sweet and it stung, then he was to do something about his acid levels. The gland in question is one that is prone to swell if someone drinks or smokes too much and creates too much acid in their body. Until late December Gary accepted their advice, but feeling much worse after Christmas he went to see his own GP. His doctor ordered a biopsy immediately. The tests showed that Gary had a cancer. He was given the news on 15th February. Two weeks later he was told he also had cancer of the lungs. For a non-smoker and a man so young this was incredible.

Ken remembers when Gary was told he had cancer. 'When Gary had finished his tests, nobody knew what was wrong with him. They thought it was laryngitis. I would never have thought in my wildest dreams that it was fatal. We went up to Carlisle to see a specialist to give him the results of a test. This specialist just came right out with it. "Look, young man, you're terminally ill, your life is limited." During the coming weeks the lad was just crying to himself all the time. In the end I was so annoyed I went and gave the consultant a piece of my mind. I said to him, "What reason and what right have you got to tell my young brother in his last weeks of life or whatever, that he's got to die and get on with it. Explain to me." He said, "Medical policy now is to inform the people that they are going to die so they can get their estate in order." I replied, "Now hang on, my brother lives in a council house, he hasn't got a bank book, living from week to week. How's he going to get his estate in order? Surely the quality of life, by not telling him, would have been better even if it is only for a week or a fortnight." You see Gary still seemed quite fit, he had lumps in his neck, but he was fit. There was an attitude that "You've got it, you can go away and cope with it yourself." But credit where it's due, Gary's GP was marvellous. For the sake of the family Gary tried very hard to keep a steady hand on his feelings.'

Gary was uncertain as to whether he would qualify for legal aid. We asked how much he earned a week: for dismantling the reactor, for risking his life, he took home the princely sum of £90 a week. We learned later that nobody had told him of his right to free prescriptions. Initially the family got little advice, legal or medical. Ken blames other workers' attitudes for the fact that Gary did not get prompt medical attention.

'I know from when I worked there of guys who have purposely cut themselves to get a sick note. Idiots! I've witnessed it. On Monday morning the surgeries are full of people with hangovers who don't want to go into work. The nurses and doctors know the tricks. Of course that was fifteen years ago and it might have changed now.'

Martyn Day, a London solicitor, took up Gary's claim and in the course of applying for legal aid he had to ask the unions if they would consider taking the case instead. The reason for this is that no funds will come from the 'public purse', legal aid, until all other remedies are exhausted. In September, some six months after the initial diagnosis, a union man made the first visit to Gary. Until that time neither plant management, welfare officer nor union representatives had been to see Gary at home. A union representative told Gary that he should not talk to CORE and that we were only in it for 'our own ends'.

Ken told me that the company started to give Gary lifts to the hospital once it was known we were involved. Of course the people who worked with Gary cared about him and they held some fund-raising events to make things easier for him in his last weeks.

The second time we saw Gary he was much worse. Whereas previously he had a little trouble drinking, he was now in terrible pain. His skin had a terrible white pallor and his face was distorted by the cancer. The legal advisers with us told Gary to make out an affidavit which would stand in court, should he not be able to give evidence. Both thought then (as indeed his family did), that he would not see the end of the month. We never saw Gary again. We kept in touch with his progress via Ken. Gary died on 27th January 1988, aged twenty-eight. Ken told us, 'Gary knew he was dying and he had a good idea Sellafield was a contributory factor towards it. I spent many, many hours with Gary. It's horrible, I wouldn't wish it on anybody to suffer. On Christmas Day, for example, we'd a family reunion in his house. My dad's a very emotional person, he couldn't go into the same room as Gary without crying. We used to bring him here just to give the family a bit of a rest. Bring him here for a week at a time, but it was a stress on us. Trying to communicate with him. Gary would be sitting in this chair, where I'm sitting now, blind, paralysed and that. If he heard you had gone out of the room he would worry and fret.'

Gary White was not the only non-smoking Sellafield worker to die of lung cancer. In 1986 a charge-hand fitter, Thomas Robinson, started proceedings against BNFL for his bronchial carcinoma. In 1984 the widow of a Mr Moore of Egremont received £120,000 for the lung cancer he contracted whilst working at Sellafield.

Les Tuley, head of BNFL information services, draws a very different picture of worker care. 'People who work at Sellafield. . . are cared for to the highest standards, not only medically, but in all other respects too. If you do a direct comparison with similar workers in other industries, then their pay is certainly amongst the top ones. In terms of medical care, we have four doctors on the site, nurses, and there is an annual medical. There is no excuse for anybody not being well looked after, because all the facilities are there and everybody is encouraged to use them. From the safety point of view, safety is looked on as an absolute priority and certainly everybody is encouraged to work in the safest possible way and always has been. The safety requirements keep going higher and higher. The techniques in working have changed tremendously since I started and are now far safer than when I started. It does not mean to say they weren't safe when I started, but we've learnt a lot, certainly in the last thirty years.'

The pressure to work at Sellafield, even for those who have doubts, is phenomenal. Most of Ken's and Gary's family have worked at Sellafield at some time or another and one of the four brothers is still employed on the construction site. Ken's father, a semi-skilled labourer, used to work on site too. Brought up on a council estate at Whitehaven in a typically working class household, Ken White was led to believe Sellafield would be the answer to his work problem.

'I was brought up with being told that Sellafield is "be all and end all", it's "get a job at Sellafield and be there for life". The community held it up like a god. It wasn't until I actually got there and worked there, not for BNFL, but as a sub-contractor, that I began to see just what exactly happened there. They had very little industry other than the mines which were going. Also the contrast with the clean environment, as everybody said of working in Sellafield, to tunnelling down a mine, was completely different. So people generally tended to think of Sellafield as good conditions and good wages. People are generally afraid to speak up because of jobs. I feel disgusted to be quite honest. The trouble is Sellafield has been there many years now and you've got whole families working in the damn place and they are all indoctrinated the same. I did seven years down there, seven years too long. I must be quite honest, I was in the same frame of mind as probably a lot of people who work there. It's a steady wage. I remember vividly the day I packed it in. I came home and Janice said, "What are you doing home?" I said, "I'm finished, I've had enough of the place." You could literally see the tears in her eyes. She asked, "Well, how are we going to pay the mortgage, how are we going to live?" As if it was the end of the world. At that time I thought, "It *is* the end of the world, what am I going to do?" Fifteen years later and I've never looked back. I'm one who's done it, but there's 4,000 guys down there with offspring who won't do it you know.'

Ken was a construction worker within the separation area, which is where the radioactive materials are handled. Because of that he wore a radiation badge all the time. The construction workers outside the area do not wear radiation-monitoring badges. In the past this has led to stoppages and strikes over the worries of radioactive releases. Construction workers have been concerned that they would not be dealt with properly if there were an accident. The memories of those workers unwittingly slaving away building Calder Hall while the old Plutonium Piles emitted huge amounts of radioactivity still haunt a number of the men.

In February 1986 eight hundred construction workers walked off-site when they discovered they had not been told of the amber alert that had happened in the reprocessing plant B205. It was some twenty-four hours later that BNFL admitted that some plutonium nitrate had escaped from the building (e/m 8/2/89). The discharge of plutonium was equivalent to two days' normal discharge. Film shot shortly before the accident by a local TV station showed holes in the windows of B205. So much for the filter system. One worker told me that at the time of Chernobyl fallout passing over the plant, 'A few alarms went off and we all took the standard procedure, nobody seemed to panic. Anyway, we came out of the building and some people had left their building. I said to the person next to me, 'Even we're not so bloody stupid as to have several leaks at once!' Then the monitors came to tell us it was outside contamination and that we could go back in. We were sat discussing the Russian business, and 1957, when it dawned on us that if there was a major accident on site that our air would be drawn in from a contaminated atmosphere outside and that the alarms would only go off after the air had been through our building. I suppose they must have some sort of shut-off mechanism for the actual air intake, but it certainly made me worry.'

If there are health worries they are well equalled by fears over job losses. 14,000 people work on site in all. 7,000 belong to BNFL and the UKAEA and the rest work for various construction firms. There has been an ongoing battle, between the local people and the unions on one side and BNFL management on the other, to get more West Cumbrians employed. By November 1983 more than half the men on the massive THORP construction project were from outside the area. Locals were expected to make up only 63 per cent of the 4,000 men that would be employed on the site. Everybody accepted that there was a shortage of the relevant skills amongst local men, yet no moves were made to get a skill centre for the area. BNFL claims that almost 90 per cent of its own workforce are local people, but quite what is meant by local any more is something of a mystery. So many construction workers and scientists settled in the area when the plant first started that they are now regarded as 'locals'. Almost like the increasing levels of radioactivity which add to 'background levels', the off-comers have become incorporated with the indigenous population. No one can turn back the clock and no one would want to remove thousands of settled families, but as with everything else at Sellafield, the workforce is mainly an imported material not natural to the area and thus part of the setting of a false economy.

In 1984 the local paper reported 3,000 people vying for 100 jobs at Sellafield. The jobs, for health physics monitors and process workers, were in the new Pond 5 complex. Fifty of the applications came from some of the 520 Haig Pit miners who were facing redundancy (w/n 24.5.85).

By March 1985 the 'Jobs For Locals' issue reached a head. Union leaders and councillors united with other people to protest at outsiders being given jobs at Sellafield. An 'Action for Jobs' campaign was set up to press the issue home. The most depressing, but truthful, comment came from Alec Morton, the chairman, who told the first meeting of the campaign: 'We are living in a nuclear dustbin and we at least deserve the right to work in it. Walking down Egremont main street all you meet are Geordie contractors working for BNFL. Yet there are men out-of-work living in the same town who can do the jobs.' 800 people attended the subsequent rally and some 200, mainly unemployed people, walked the six miles from Egremont to the plant. However a local GMB official noted, 'In five years' time this place will be finished with jobs and where will we march to then?' (w/n 18.4.85). A lot of people feel particularly angry about the £80 to £90 lodging subsistence paid to travelling men which could be saved by employing locals. In fact to some people, like Gary White, that was almost a week's take-home pay. The presence of the BNFL hostels for construction workers show the company are eager to cater for off-comers. However what few realise is that those hostels are there to discourage construction workers settling in the area. Thus when they become unemployed they show up as a statistic many miles away from the site they are laid off from.

The nuclear industry, in one form or another, has become very important to Cumbria. Consider the statistics. This county has the lowest population per square mile in England. At Vickers shipbuilders in Barrow, where Trident is being built, there are 13,500 workers, 37 per cent of the working population of the area. In Copeland BNFL employs 33 per cent of the working population. The County Council itself employs more people than either company, but spends less than either of the above companies. There is no doubt that in the atomic age Cumbria has become the nuclear county.

CHAPTER

3

We owe respect to the living; to the dead we owe nothing but truth.
'Lettres Sur Oedipe', Voltaire

Since its inception the nuclear industry has tried to improve its medical care whilst at the same time keeping the industry competitive. As a company BNFL claims its policy towards its workforce is one of the best there is. Radiation exposure is kept within the statutes laid down. The rule is that radiation doses are 'as low as reasonably practicable' and must fall within the limit laid down by the International Commission on Radiological Protection. The current legal limit is set at 50 milli-Sieverts (mSv) per annum for a worker, three times more than the National Radiological Protection Board's recommended level of 15 mSv. A Sievert is a measure of the amount of radiation taken into the body either externally or internally. If an employee's day-to-day work might cause an exposure to exceed the lower, recommended level, then that worker's details go on the radiation register. Only workers receiving over 15 mSv per annum are given annual medical check-ups. Nobody is allowed a radiation dose inside the industry under the age of eighteen. The company also undertakes certain practical measures to reduce exposure. The first is to ensure adequate shielding for the workers from radioactive material. To measure external radiation exposure, workers wear radiation badges which can detect gamma and beta radiations, which are very penetrating. In certain parts of the plant personal air samplers, which measure radioactivity in the air, give an idea of how much alpha radioactivity a worker might be taking in. In the more radioactive parts of the plant, face masks are worn with full radiation suits, known as Windscale suits, along with a radiation badge and a personal air sampler. Thus where radiation exposures do occur, they can be measured. Workers are also asked, from time to time, to give samples of urine and faeces for testing and the radiation doses to the internal organs can be assessed.

Every year BNFL's own reports show the majority of their nuclear workers receive less than 50 mSv although a percentage of the workforce, which can vary each year, does receive above the recommended 15 mSv. A small number of the workforce receive near to the limit. A worker can exceed the permitted radiation dose for internal and/or external radiation. If they are contaminated internally they are taken off work in the active area until tests on urine and faeces show that they can resume normal duties. With external radiation workers are kept from the area for a set period of time.

In 1982 the Greenpeace report on cancer deaths in Cumbria was discussed with Japanese scientists. They were appalled to learn that, in 1981, 1,100 Sellafield workers received between 1.5 and 2 rads (units of absorbed radiation) per annum in their work. The Japanese had estimated that people two miles from the epicentre of the Hiroshima blast had received a dose of 1.9 rads. Of course, the Sellafield doses were received over a much longer period, but it is believed by many scientists that small doses over a longer period are far worse than large, single doses (e/m 14.8.82). The most recent information suggests that exposure to the legal radiation dose makes the nuclear industry six times as risky as other high risk industries.

The company has a full-time labour officer on site who liaises with the unions and management over worker problems. Workers are fully advised of their rights. The unions also complement the health and safety work of the company by running TUC courses on general safety at work, advising workers of their rights (all the while stressing the importance of union membership) and funding or backing cases where necessary.

BNFL operates a compensation scheme with the unions whereby, under certain circumstances, compensation is paid for certain cancers that are thought to be radiation-linked. No proof has been established that BNFL has caused a worker cancer. The unions are proud of the scheme because it shows a marked step forward in worker/management relations and also means that relatives are relieved of the burden of long and sometimes distressing court actions. The unions believe the positive points of the scheme are that they get claims settled quicker, with less cost to both sides and less distress to the families involved. Further, the panel which adjudicates on the scheme pays out on 30 per cent and 40 per cent probabilities, whereas the court always has to have a 51 per cent burden of proof. Both the unions and BNFL operate a screening process which eliminates those cases which they feel do not fit into the prescribed rules as laid down by the scheme.

Obviously a company policy, no matter how much it is supported by a union, cannot be adhered to 100 per cent. With the best will in the world there are practical difficulties that arise in monitoring exact radiation doses for thousands of workers over a forty year period. Not only do workers admit to having failed in reporting all their own exposure in the past, but at times of accidents an ensuing panic can lead to vital things being overlooked. Workers, sometimes for the best of reasons (to save another worker) or for the worst of reasons (pure idleness) take measures that do not fit into the code of practice.

Thus the whole issue of relating worker doses to the cancer, at a given age, in the compensation scheme can be flawed. The most glaring iniquity in the scheme was that a living worker could not claim under it! In April 1988 the scheme was changed to allow not only live British Nuclear Fuels Limited workers, but also United Kingdom Atomic Energy Authority employees, the right to claim. Ministry of Defence, Central Electricity Generating Board and South of Scotland Electricity Board workers were all excluded. Yet the unions which negotiated the deal have members in all sections of the industry. Another criticism levelled at the compensation scheme is that if a case survives the screening process of the unions and management the 'expert panel' often simply uses a slide rule technique to judge a case. Therefore their 'expertise' is very rarely put to use. Not that we can question their expertise as they (along with the details of the compensation scheme itself) are secret. Other problems are that a worker has no right to employ a solicitor to present a claim to the panel, or any right of appeal. All claims are dealt with via the unions, and all the proceedings of the panel are conducted in writing.

Tony Hildrop, who used to be a shop steward on site, recalls that things were very different at one time. 'In the early days the wages were poor. You had to fight quite hard for it. I'm proud of the part that I played in improving the conditions and the wages. I am also very proud that I played a part in the compensation agreement. It broke new ground in trade union negotiations. We were fighting for at least seven years for it. When I hear people say the unions are in the company pocket it gets me annoyed, because I know the fight that we had. I know from hard experience, it's something we've had to work at. There is no way the unions caved in. They are still fighting like blazes to not only maintain the conditions they have but to improve it. I have seen people with cancer. It's something which can't be proved, that's why we argue the probability of cases in the scheme. The chances of someone getting into the industry with a serious illness is very remote. The thing that annoys me are the irresponsible statements which are made about cancer connected with the atomic energy industry. If it was as cancer-producing as it's accused of being, then why hasn't the workforce got a high incidence of cancer? In fact it is well below the national average. In general the safety standards at Sellafield are extremely high.'

There are those who believe there is a link. As early as 1975, the Electrical Trades Union secretary, T. McBride, told the South West Cumbria Health Authority that, 'We have members who have died at Windscale. On their death certificates it says the cause of death is radioactivity. No matter what anyone might say to the contrary, we can produce these certificates.' (e/m 23.12.75).

BNFL and the unions feel quite happy about the health of the workers within BNFL sites. Cancer mortality studies undertaken by the company have shown that the workforce enjoys a cancer rate less than that of the general public. This is due to what is known as the 'healthy worker effect'. Most BNFL workers are of an age, social grouping and income bracket which means that they are generally healthier than the population at large. A more accurate assessment would be to compare the BNFL workers with a similar number of workers in a biscuit factory of the same age group. It is impossible to know whether the cancers experienced relate to what job and what dose rates since the company refuses publicly to disclose this type of information. Professor Edward Radford, a radiation expert who once worked with the Hiroshima Effects Research Foundation, said that analysis of the BNFL mortality figures showed a 30 per cent increase above the norm in the cancer rate for the 'retirals' group. This would accord with the view that, because of the long-latency period of cancers caused by radiation, the company cannot claim to have a healthy workforce simply because the workers do not fall ill immediately after exposure.

Some workers have told CORE that there are certain workers who believe the compensation scheme is an 'easy way out'. Some don't worry too much at work about regulations as they believe their families will be compensated in the event of them dying of cancer. However, this is very far from the truth. Approximately 200 cases have actually got as far as the screening process, and of those only fifteen have been paid out.

In 1987 the unions decided to pursue a case of compensation through the courts for Albert Pattinson, who had developed Hodgkin's disease. He and three other men in the B3 workshop had contracted the disease. Pattinson was one of forty workers permanently restricted from receiving any further radiation doses. He had been exposed to airborne plutonium during an accident. He had started work in Sellafield in 1954 and according to his records had received 67 per cent of the International Commission for Radiological Protection limit for a worker (g 7.7.87). His claim was dropped mid-way through the court case due to a lack of medical statistical evidence. Pattinson is still working at Sellafield. It is presumed he will be pursuing the case under the compensation scheme now that it includes live workers.

One of the four in the workshop died of Hodgkin's disease aged thirty-two. His widow was left with a young son to bring up. No other claims for this illness have yet been settled. The latest review of the scheme will take account of the recent information from Japan which suggests that radiation is three or even five times more dangerous than once thought. The level of radiation exposure at which a case qualifies for compensation is now being reduced. Theoretically more people will now qualify.

There have been worries over the length of time it takes to settle a claim. As early as 1976 Bill Baptist, then the GMB's regional organiser, was saying, 'Here we have forty cases and, as a union, we may not take action for twenty years, perhaps less, depending if and when the effect of the exposure they have undeniably undergone, manifests itself. As the law and procedure stand now, if a worker has a breakdown in health in twenty years' time and can relate it to twenty years ago in terms of exposure he can claim, but by that time he may be nearly in his grave.' (e/m 23.11.76).

Many of them, like Jonathon Troughton from Millom, are already in their graves. In September 1975 Troughton was awarded benefits by a DHSS panel on the basis that his multiple myeloma was an industrial injury. In 1976 the unions started to fight for an amendment to the legislation to allow workers withdrawn from 'active area' work to be awarded loss of danger pay (e/m 7.9.76). At the time 192 men were suffering loss of earnings because they had been taken out of the active area. 152 were on six months' 'suspension' of active area work and the other forty were permanently restricted and would never work with radioactive materials again. Troughton's case, along with two others, was chosen by the unions to go forward as test cases.

Ian Robertson, the union solicitor, had to issue a summons in court to make BNFL release the records of Malcolm Pattinson, a worker who had leukaemia (g 12.11.76). Pattinson's widow eventually received £67,000 for her husband's illness.

The industry would never have settled for a low key, out of court procedure, had there not been widows willing to fight cases the hard way. One such woman was Joan King. Joan lived in the large council estate in Egremont. Many of the blue-collar workers live here. Some, like Joan's husband, Harry King, settled down to raise a family and work in the new hi-tech industry of the day – such was the nuclear industry's promise.

Joan was a local woman. She had the strong accent of a West Cumbrian which would easily distinguish her from any other part of the county. Like most West Cumbrians she had a ready, if at times harsh humour, which saw her through many a bleak period. There was no humour in her when she related the story of her husband and how he died.

Harry King died on 12th May 1973 of a brain tumour. He was fifty years old. Joan received £8,000 in compensation. This was paid without prejudice and the company said it was not an admission of liability. The union, the General and Municipal Workers (as then was) had taken up two cases, Troughton's and King's, as they felt that they might stand a chance of success with them in the courts.

Joan was very bitter about her husband's settlement. Ever since his death Joan had been an eager and outspoken critic of BNFL. She had seen a dearly loved husband destroyed by a long and painful illness. She had to stand by as a fine and healthy man, an active union representative (who had also been a town councillor) was reduced to an agonised human being who, at times, failed even to recognise his own family. Joan knew that you cannot quantify such suffering in monetary terms. But she also knew that life for her and the children would have been easier had she had more money. Joan was ever anxious to point out that she was not interested in the money for herself, but that she would have liked more to spend on her grandchild, something she would have been able to do had she still had an active and working husband.

Harry had been forced to retire from Sellafield through ill health in 1971. He had worked at Sellafield for twenty years. Up until 1961 he had worked in the plutonium area. Post-mortem reports confirmed the cause of death, although the subsequent coroner's verdict was left open as he felt he could not attribute the cause of death to Harry's work at Sellafield. BNFL had requested Harry's internal organs for them to test to establish the radioactivity content. Joan says that she found this one of the most disturbing and distressing aspects of the whole case. The analysis, undertaken by Dr Geoff Schofield, showed that Harry's body burden of plutonium was around 10 per cent of the international limit permitted for nuclear workers. Joan had never actually seen a copy of the coroner's report until James Cutler (producer of the Yorkshire Television programme 'Windscale – the Nuclear Laundry') obtained it for her.

Joan told me, 'Harry started working at Sellafield in February 1951. It hadn't been long in production. For a short while he was on security and then he was moved to reprocessing. He didn't talk a lot about what was happening. He was contaminated once or twice, he'd come home saying he had to be scrubbed. He didn't seem unduly worried until about 1961, just about the time our youngest daughter was born. He said they'd found rather a high plutonium content in the building where he'd been working. They moved all the men at that time out of the building for good because they'd been inhaling plutonium dust. He was told he'd a full body burden of plutonium at the time. As the years went by the first thing we noticed was that his teeth were separating from the gums. The dentist who examined his teeth said they would have to all come out, but he also said he couldn't understand it as there was no decay of the teeth or infection of the gums. At the same time as this was happening he was losing his hair. I remember the day we were watching TV and he said to me, 'I can see double'. Just prior to that there'd been a programme on about cataracts and I went and looked in his eye and I said in my opinion Harry you've got a cataract. He told me not to be so silly. He saw the doctor and there was a cataract.

'When the cataract was removed the retina was dislodged, it had gone right through. They tried several different ways of fastening the retina on but it kept haemorrhaging. No sooner had they given up on this eye than they started on the other and he was completely blind in one eye. Two visits to an eminent eye surgeon at Moorfields in London and there was no more they could do for him. The union, the GMB, started a claim for compensation for loss of his eyesight. He retired at forty-eight, he started to learn Braille, but all the time the union were trying to fight for his injuries. Before this bore any fruit he took bad, in December '72. We noticed he was getting confused in what he was talking about, he was getting mixed up. Dr Willey, whose main work at West Cumberland Hospital was as heart specialist, saw him. He said, "I'm sorry, but your husband is seriously ill and I wouldn't know how to treat plutonium cases." He referred us to Mr Shaw, a new surgeon at Newcastle Hospital. Harry entered Newcastle Hospital, just for an examination. When we went to visit Dr Shaw told me Harry had a massive brain tumour and there was nothing they could do. When Harry died and BNFL did tests for plutonium content they said it was too low to do my husband any damage. The inquest brought in an open verdict and said there was insufficient evidence to show cause. The unions got Ian Robertson, the solicitor, who pursued a compensation claim, that was 1973.

'On November 15th 1977 I was summoned to Carlisle High Court – really it was a hearing on Jonathon Troughton who'd died later than Harry with multiple myeloma. They were bringing his case forward first, they said it was a stronger case. When I met the solicitor I was told that an offer had been made on Harry's case that morning. The most they would offer was £8,000, which according to the figures was one-third of the amount that they worked out, taking into account Harry's age and working life, he would have had. It was quite a surprise for me. I was by myself and I had nobody with me to advise me and I just asked the union solicitor what should I do. I couldn't take it in. He said when your case comes up you could lose it. I didn't want to accept the offer and yet I thought I might end up with nothing. Lean years took their toll. I suppose that's why I accepted the deal. Since then there's been a lot of other cases of various cancers and leukaemias and so on. Maybe through the test cases, mine and Mrs Troughton's, maybe it's helped get a better deal. One of the later cases to get paid out was my cousin's husband.

'During our marriage we were both active in local politics. We were in the Labour Party, we believed in what we were doing. If we could improve things in the town that was our main aim. During Harry's illness, apart from one union rep, very few others came to see how he was. For quite a few years Harry was a shop steward. He was a union member. I was really disappointed.'

Joan was not the sort of woman to become dispirited easily, even though she had known other sadness than losing Harry. 'During our marriage we'd had five children altogether. The first was a little girl who contracted meningitis at four months and we lost her. Then we had a little boy who was born normal, but he was accidentally drowned at two and a half when I was three months pregnant with my eldest daughter, so out of my five children I have two daughters and a son. I'm glad I have them. One's now 37, the boy is 33 and the youngest is 27 just this year. Harry and I kept a close-knit family, we didn't go out without them, we didn't go on our own holidays without them. He was a family man, he didn't go out drinking. We used to go for long walks before we could afford a car.

'People ask why don't I move to get away from the place. I love the place I was born in. Rather I used to love it, I don't love it now. I stay here because my family is here. I was here before Sellafield and I'm not moving for them. My father's side of the family were Cumbrians from way, way back. In fact my great-aunt was a cousin of John Peel's! The reason I speak out against anything nuclear is I don't want to see what happened to my husband and a lot of his friends happen to anybody else.

Unfortunately there's one of his friends getting radiation treatment now, so it's still going on, it's still happening.'

Joan thought that perhaps the case could be reviewed. This would rest on two points. Firstly that the compensation scheme now in operation might have a more enlightened view and that since lower dose rates were now accepted as causing more cancer Harry's claim might be set at a higher level. Secondly that the claims for Harry's cataracts, which the union had been pursuing until his cancer was diagnosed, had never been settled.

Joan had corresponded with the solicitors over the actual basis upon which the case would be fought. She had been told that the union would be asking for somewhere in the region of £24,000 for Harry's case. She knew Jonathon Troughton's case might do better than Harry's, but only because Troughton had died from multiple myeloma. However, Harry had worked the same length of time in the plutonium area as Troughton and she felt that the compensation paid should be roughly equal. After the case a sympathetic union man gave Joan a copy of a letter which had been sent from the solicitors to the regional representatives of the GMWU. Although the solicitors were not happy to get less than the full amount asked for, they were glad that compensation had been paid. 'BNFL had always maintained that there has never been any proof that an employee has contracted a cancer or other illness as a result of being contaminated by radiation at Windscale (or elsewhere in the country); that claim can no longer be made. The *Daily Telegraph* described the cases as being historic and they may prove to be so.'

The letter went on, 'I was asked if we would be prepared to discontinue the case of King if Troughton's case was settled. I refused such a suggestion without even seeking your instructions.' The letter continued, 'It was up to BNFL to make an offer if they did not want the case to be heard. I knew that the Windscale evidence being given at the inquiry at Whitehaven would be coming to an end and that BNFL would not want detailed medical evidence *re* King given in the High Court and felt at this stage that they might pay a third of the full value.'

Joan had tried by herself to get the case reviewed under the compensation agreement, but with no success. Jack Cunningham MP, so sympathetic in earlier days, was unable to offer any help.

Joan said, 'When I think of all the support that Harry and I gave the unions and the Labour Party in this area. You know, I even knitted bootees for Jack's first child. People say you're grasping because you want a case re-opening, but it's not that. It's the injustice of it all. They're too blind to see that one day it could be them. Keeping your mouth shut does no good nowadays. I think that's what really riles them. I should have been a good little widow woman who was ever so grateful for the pittance from the great BNFL. I should have come home and been a good, quiet girl. But I wanted to let people know what the plant does. I want to expose the secrecy surrounding the place. I know we're poor people here, but not so poor that we have to sell our souls to that place. When I think of what they did to a good man, well, it's enough to make you weep.'

When I began to write this book I wanted people to know what Joan was like. To meet her, a lively and active woman, is to realise what a true survivor she is. But life became too much for Joan, and in March 1989 she took her own life.

The jubilation over Harry King's getting compensation might well be thought natural enough, but what is strange is that everyone should consider Troughton and King's case to be the first. In fact the first case ever paid out, which was publicly acknowledged, was to the widow of Bernard Clarke in 1960. She was awarded £4,000 for her husband's myeloid leukaemia. This had been diagnosed as early as 1956 and Clarke had in fact started legal proceedings before he died. Clarke also suffered from cataracts. This case is astounding because most leukaemias have a 'gestation' period of two or three years, which means Clarke must have received very high doses in the early days of the plant. Most people believe that in the early days people simply weren't getting big enough doses to cause illnesses. However, the UKAEA paid in an out-of-court settlement. Another person paid compensation in the early days, although it was never stated why, was Peter Nugent. He lived to the ripe old age of eighty, although in 1952 he had swallowed eighty times the safe annual dose of plutonium! The fact that he was paid only came to light at his inquest, as the payment had been kept secret under the Official Secrets Act.

In 1985 the unions were still expressing concern that compensation cases were taking too long to be paid out. Bill Maxwell, the

GMB chief convenor on site, said, 'In some cases the next of kin could be dead themselves before a settlement is made. The compensation scheme is a good thing and it means that claims in respect of radiation victims do not have to be made in court. But the whole process needs to be speeded up. Cases suitable for compensation could be lost in antiquity before a payout is agreed. There are dozens of cases in the pipeline, some going back nearly thirty years. There should be an immediate review of the scheme. It is far too slow and cumbersome. Since the scheme started the Institute of Professional Civil Servants has had three cases and my union, which instigated the scheme, has had no agreed settlements. The idea was to speed up cases. There must be a flaw in the system.' One such case was that of Doris Burns of Egremont, who was not paid until December 1983 for her husband's leukaemia. He had died in 1965 and she had had to wait eighteen years for a payment. Doris was the first to be paid under the compensation scheme.

Maxwell was also worried that not only were there delays, but that other illnesses caused by radiation were not being considered. 'There has been no payout to the widow of Stan Higgins of Whitehaven, who was referred to as Windscale's "Radioactive Man" after exposure to radiation before he died of a heart attack in 1979 aged fifty. I think it should be recognised that there are cases other than cancer victims which could be examined under the compensation scheme. There are cases where workers have had very high radiation doses and could be said to have suffered the effects of their work. Yet because the cause of death was not cancer they have not fallen within this scheme.' (w/n 28.3.85) (e/m 29.3.85).

What is little known is that the union had tried investigations into such a case in the mid-seventies. Bill Rickleton, the Northern Regional Secretary of the GMB, confirmed then that an eleven-year-old boy's case of heart defect was to be looked at because the father had been exposed to radiation. 'This is one of several cases we have been investigating. We are having a conference with counsel and solicitors to determine the number of experts we can bring forward. We have a number of genetic experts and it is a question of selecting the evidence.' The case was to be based on the father having suffered sperm damage. Rickleton commented,

'In three cases we are going hard for the line in that they (the workers) went in there (Sellafield) healthy and they were damaged. We want to go back two hundred years and say that when any man enters an employer's premises fit in body and mind, if he comes out of there damaged in any way then it will be taken as a *prima facie* case that he has been damaged at work. This is the American precedent and they still use it. Therefore instead of us having to prove that the employer was negligent, the employer has to prove that he took all the precautions, including training the man for the job.' (e/m 5.10.76). Since then the father in question has died of pancreatic cancer and the son died in his mid-twenties of heart disease.

In September 1986 BNFL paid out three more workers. £75,000 for a lung cancer victim who died in 1969 and £31,529 to a worker who had died of liver cancer in 1973. No details of the third case were released (e/m 16.9.86). In November 1984 the company paid out £25,000 for a Springfields worker who died of leukaemia. In all some £500,000 has been paid out to BNFL workers in cases before and after the scheme began. None of these payments seemed to come to Gavin Laird's mind when he wrote defending the industry in 1986. The shockwaves of Chernobyl were still being felt in the unions and the General Secretary of the AEU, Sellafield's second largest trade union, was anxious to pacify people. In a special union editorial he wrote, 'Britain has generated electricity using nuclear power for over twenty-five years. During that time there has not been a single fatality to a member of staff at any of the civil nuclear installations resulting from radiation hazards. Since 1956, when nuclear energy was first used to generate electricity, no member of the public has died or been injured as a result of an accident involving radioactivity at a nuclear power station.' (AEU Journal Oct. 1986).

In November 1983 the first of three very important Sellafield inquests was held. Ken Roberts had died of multiple myeloma, a bone marrow cancer whose only known cause in any age group is radiation. It is specifically linked with plutonium, a radioactive heavy metal which concentrates on to the bone surface and bone endings. The inquest heard that Roberts had plutonium, caesium and cerium in his body. He had worked at Sellafield from 1964, but before that he'd been at Springfields and also on other nuclear work for the Ministry of Supply. He had been receiving industrial injuries benefit before he died because of his illness. Dr Berrill, from the local hospital, giving evidence at the inquest, said he was 'not aware of any large increase in cancer patients in the area'. Dr Schofield, BNFL's chief medical officer, said that analysis of Roberts' organs had found levels of contamination five times higher than in members of the public, but that these were still exceedingly small quantities. The jury returned an 'open verdict' on Roberts' cause of death.

The coroner, Mr Walker, asked the jury to try to block from their minds the YTV programme. 'Many of you will have watched the recent television programme. I ask you to forget that programme, it is perhaps no value whatsoever. The connection between these diseases and Windscale is not yet proven.' And yet multiple myeloma victims had already received compensation from BNFL although without any admission of liability.

The BNFL mortality study on its own workers had shown that during the thirty-two years from 1948–80 only four cases of multiple myeloma were recorded in their workers. This compares to 4.1 expected in a general population group of the same number. This puts the rate at one case per eight years.

In the following year, 1984, an inquest was held on the death of Joseph Corrie who had died at the age of sixty of multiple myeloma. He had worked immediately under No. 1 Pile in 1957. Schofield had said that tests in Corrie's liver, lungs and bones showed levels of plutonium between five and ten times those in the general public, but they were extremely small quantities. The jury thought there was not a high incidence of multiple myeloma at the plant as BNFL's medical chief, Dr Geoffrey Schofield, had told the jury that the rate of multiple myeloma at the plant was the same as that expected amongst an equal number of the general population. There was, therefore, no link with Sellafield and Corrie's death. The jury came back with an open verdict. Following that inquest CORE tackled BNFL over its multiple myeloma rate. Schofield 'found' another case of this cancer which had been overlooked on their records. We also know that in the years 1981–84 four cases of the cancer had occurred within the workforce, thus bringing the rate from one in every eight years to approximately one every year. BNFL said they would not comment on this as they did not know the expected rate of the disease within the general population for that same period! Yet BNFL believed they knew enough to say there was no increase in multiple myeloma. Surely what looks like an eight-fold increase warranted further investigation? We publicised this information on the extra cases since 1981.

Schofield had also ignored a 1977 report from the National Radiological Protection Board (NRPB) suggesting that bone marrow diseases were high at the plant. Within the workforce they had found twelve cases of bone marrow-related disease, where only six should have been found. Their numbers are higher than those in the mortality report because not all of those with the illness were dead. On statistical tests there is only a one in ten chance that the excess would occur randomly (g 10.2.77).

In October 1984 the inquest was held on ex-Sellafield worker Isaac McAllister, who had died aged sixty-seven of multiple myeloma. The inquest was told that McAllister had twice been removed from 'the area' because he had been overexposed. Schofield, who again gave evidence, said his tests had found traces of plutonium in McAllister's liver, lungs and bones. He said, 'I have expressed the opinion that the radionuclides in Mr McAllister's body could have made a small contribution to the causation of his death.' Also giving evidence at that inquest was Frank Ward, who told those present that McAllister worked in the radiation area from 1951–81 and that in those areas people could be exposed to radiation 'accidentally'. This time a verdict of industrial disease was returned. Ward, a health physicist by profession, would himself be dead of a brain tumour within eighteen months at the age of sixty.

It will have become noticeable that there are distinct trends towards worker exposure. Workers never seem to exceed legal radiation exposure although permitted levels have varied greatly over the years. Wilson, Guneratne, McAllister and all the others started work when 150mSv was the maximum limit per annum, three times more than the present legal limit and ten times more than the recommended level of 15mSv now in use. Plutonium can only be measured against the levels in the public as they take this up from food contaminated with the radioactive fallout of atmospheric nuclear weapons testing. An international ban was put on above-ground explosions in the early 1960s as it was feared that the trace limits the public were exposed to would cause harm. Yet all the worker inquests state that the increased plutonium level had no effect on them.

In 1986, a NRPB report disclosed post-mortem examinations of the internal organs of three ex-Sellafield workers showed incredibly high levels of plutonium. The average UK plutonium level for non-Cumbrian residents was 1.9 millibecquerels (a measurement of radioactivity) per kilogramme of lung. In the three worker cases it was 120, 450 and 1,140 millibecquerels. The average for Cumbrian civilians was 6.8 (g 5.8.86). After the report was published Bill Maxwell, the General, Municipal and Boilermakers Union chief convenor at Sellafield, commented, 'In my time I have seen approximately forty people who have been restricted from working with plutonium after inhaling it and these people have subsequently retired with good health.' (w/n 21.8.86). Two of those people were Troughton and King, men whom the GMB had got compensation for because they died early of cancer.

The whole question of internal contamination of workers is one which has dogged the nuclear industry, in terms of assessing radiation dose. In January 1986 the ICRP introduced new permitted levels for alpha emitters in air. Alpha radiation does not travel far and cannot penetrate into the body. Alpha emitters are most damaging when inhaled or ingested and then damage the soft tissues of internal organs. This led to BNFL having to insist that men wore face masks in the fuel handling and decanning plant B30, one of the oldest and dirtiest buildings on the site. Workers accepted that they had to wear the mask, but took industrial action in order to get the company to part with £1,000 lump sum payment and £40 a week extra, which they felt was their due. After all, they argued, if it was safe last week and dangerous this week then surely we should be compensated for working in a once-hazardous area without the right equipment? At that time they were in a position of strength as stopping work in B30 would have caused all reprocessing to halt. An ICRP report added to the union case: 'Static air samplers, even if located close to the breathing zone of workers, may not give results which adequately represent the intake of each individual worker. Static air samplers may underestimate a worker's dose by a factor which could lie between 100 and 1,000.' (g 24.11.83). The unions were, therefore, keen to have personal air samplers issued to all workers, but BNFL refused. Only a year prior to this trouble the company had opened the brand new Pond 5 complex, with the Prime Minister herself 'doing the honours'. At that time it was hoped that Pond 5 would take over from B30 in one year. By January 1986 the estimate was that it would take some seven years to clear the decanning plant, where the outer metal cladding is stripped from the fuel pod prior to reprocessing. The unions had good cause to argue for longer term protection. In 1988 there was talk that some workers might be offered extra danger money if they would be prepared to accept higher than the recommended radiation doses (e/m 17.11.88).

In 1987 the union agreed to start negotiations over 'selling' their morning tea-break. The new management had decided that the break was taking too much of a toll on productivity. By late 1988 the Electrical Engineering and Plumbers Union members were holding one day stoppages because they were finding it so difficult to work the longer hours uninterrupted in face masks in places like B30 or B205 (the main reprocessing building). It is not known what effect this is having on the work done.

In 1986 the long-awaited report on the state of worker health at Sellafield was published by the London School of Hygiene and Tropical Medicine. The report showed that there was a 65 per cent increase in the risk of workers contracting multiple myeloma. Deaths from bladder cancers and leukaemias were also raised. Overall the cancer death rate was slightly below the average, which is to be expected in a healthy working population. The report dealt only with death and not with incidence of cancer.

BNFL have always maintained that there is no problem with worker health because their safety precautions will protect them. In 1974 Dr Schofield and Dr Dolphin (of the NRPB) were involved in a study of the remains of ten plutonium workers which concluded that the cancer rate was normal. Of the ten workers six had died of coronary thrombosis. But in fact whenever you get a coronary thrombosis arteriosclerosis (hardening of the arteries) is also present. In a paper by Professor Edward Martell of the US National Centre for Atmospheric Research it is said that arteriosclerosis are tiny benign tumours of the arteries. Martell said that this could come about because alpha emitters concentrate in the arteries. It is thought that this concentration causes heart attacks in smokers as Polonium-210 (a naturally occurring alpha emitter) is released into the lungs when smoke is inhaled. It then finds its way to the arteries and causes the small tumours mentioned above.

Dr Rosalie Bertell, a Canadian expert on radiation, has said it is not inconceivable, in fact it is highly likely, that the same thing happens with man-made alpha emitters. (2nd National Conference Health Effects of Low Level Radiation 1986). None of this was mentioned in the Schofield/Dolphin report, yet the idea had first been raised in 1966 in the Journal of Radiology by Elkeles. Since that time Dolphin has died, aged 53, of cancer, and Schofield died in June 1985 aged 60, of a coronary. It is conceivable that the inhalation and ingestion of alpha emitters might well cause coronaries. Yet the nuclear industry insists that cancer is the only possible health effect.

Not all the cases are straightforward cancer claims. One such is that of Edward Clarke, who died of stomach cancer in 1984. His widow, Susan, is a hard-working woman bringing up a family. Like the other widows Susan was keen to impress on us that she was not pursuing a mercenary vendetta against BNFL, but that she felt taking a case against them would be the only way to get them to admit responsibility for what happened after her husband's death.

Edward Clarke worked as a rigger on decommissioning the Advanced Gas-Cooled Reactor (AGR) at Sellafield. Although the operation is run, for the most part, by the United Kingdom Atomic Energy Authority, some BNFL workers are on that part of the Sellafield site. In May 1984 Edward Clarke had fallen on some scaffolding and hurt his back. What seemed to be a relatively minor injury took some time for him to recover from. During the course of the investigations into why he was still ill three months after the fall, the doctor diagnosed cancer of the prostate with secondary cancers throughout the body.

Susan Clarke nursed her husband as best she could. 'He had first taken ill with this burst ulcer. Part of his stomach was taken away and the drainage tube was still open and he was off for about twelve or thirteen weeks. Then he went back to work with this drainage tube still open and he was treated for it there. He got the dressing put on at Sellafield which I thought was wrong. I honestly thought they would send him back home as the thing was still leaking. All I knew was no heavy lifting was allowed. He was not to wear PVC suits and was not allowed in the radioactive area. But he was back in the area inside a fortnight and he was still getting his extra money for being in the area. Then he had the accident whilst he was working in the AGR. Because he had had a lumbar fracture to the spine the doctors kept putting his pain down to this, until finally he could not walk at all and he was completely paralysed. Three days after he had become paralysed they took him through to Newcastle General when they diagnosed the cancer. Eddy was ill for eighteen months before his death. We did not see much of the Sellafield people during this time. Just once, once they came to see my husband and they said they'd got him another job, a light job, in the stores. I told the man who had come, I said that Eddy would not be going back to work. He said, "Well, I know, but it was just a rumour, but now you've told us." Whether they had come to confirm if he did have cancer or not I don't know.'

'At first I hadn't told him he had a cancer. When he had left Newcastle Hospital after tests he couldn't walk. But he fought to walk again later and even drove his car. But when he got a letter from the solicitor dealing with his back injury claim the truth came out. It said, "Mr Edwards, the orthopaedic surgeon, has told us that what you suffered from was a compression fracture of your lumbar spine, which occurred not only because of the sudden weight imposed upon your back by the movement of the plug, but also because you were at the time of the accident already suffering from a greatly weakened spine, due to a condition which was quite unrelated to the accident itself." He said to me, "What's this other illness I've got?" so I had to tell him.'

As his illness progressed Edward did speak to his wife about it. He told her that whatever happened she was to sue BNFL. Because of this the process of looking at his radiation records, to try to establish a claim, started in mid-1985. The union man dealing with the claim was Bill Robinson, AUEW convenor on site.

Edward Clarke died at 11.45 on the morning of Sunday, 3rd December 1984. At 12 noon Mrs Clarke got her brother-in-law to ask for a post-mortem to be carried out. Since it was a Sunday the post-mortem was not actually performed until the morning of Tuesday 5th.

Susan explained, 'We were later told that if we wanted to go and see Eddy for the last time then it should be the Monday night because after that we would not be allowed to see the body. As he was to be buried on the Wednesday they would be doing the post-mortem on Tuesday morning. They don't let you see the body after a post-mortem.'

This fairly straightforward post-mortem was carried out by the consultant pathologist of West Cumberland Pathology Laboratory. The cause of death is recorded as pulmonary infarction, due to deep vein thrombosis, then cancer of the prostate which had led to secondary cancer throughout the body.

Early on the Tuesday afternoon the body was laid out by the undertaker ready for burial at 1 p.m. the following day. On the morning of the funeral Susan Clarke was at home with the mourners waiting for the hearse.

'On the day of the funeral, which was the Wednesday, we got a phone call about five minutes before the hearse was due here to say the funeral was being delayed. It was the undertaker phoning from West Cumberland Hospital. They said there was a complication and they would not release the body and that he (the undertaker) would explain when he came up to see us. When he did come to see me he said, "I don't know what has happened here, the body had been moved from where I left him. I honestly don't know what's happened. But it's been tampered with." Within an hour and a half we got another phone call to say they'd released the body, you can have it!

'Eventually we had a letter from BNFL saying that one of our family requested a second post-mortem, but that's not true. In fact until that letter nobody else had even mentioned a second post-mortem, just that the organs had been taken. It seems Dr Schofield, who was head of BNFL's medical department at Sellafield, had carried out a second post-mortem and removed some of his organs. Nobody asked my permission. I said that surely someone else could not go in and do it. I was the one that requested the first post-mortem and this was the only one done as far as I was aware until the funeral. When my daughter spoke to the pathologist on the phone she asked him how long Eddy had had the cancer. He said it was a fairly rapid cancer. They told me that in Newcastle as well, that it was a fast cancer, yet Sellafield, according to their letters it could have stemmed from any time – it can be carried in the body for such a long time. If Eddy had had it for such a long time how come they hadn't spotted it when he started to work there?

'Eddy was a fine, healthy man. He played rugby, he also had hound dogs, trail hounds, which he liked to take to meetings. It got to be he couldn't take them for a walk. So many things he could not do any more. He was only fifty-six, he should have had years ahead of him. He aged ten years in twelve months. He wasn't a small man, but he just seemed to shrink to nothing, there was nothing of him in the end.'

In the letter from BNFL to the family about the second post-mortem BNFL said the request had come via the coroner's office who, BNFL state, had said that a member of the family had requested it be done. Susan Clarke has never found out who it was from the coroner's office who had said this, nor has the mysterious member of the family ever come to light. BNFL has failed to name the person who made the request.

In the immediate aftermath of this episode Susan could not think straight. She asked the union what she should do about the expenses for the funeral breakfast that had been wasted. The union approached BNFL who agreed to pay, but pointed out that this was no admission of liability that they had caused the delay in the burial.

A claim is now being pursued against the company with regard to the taking of organs without the family's permission. Susan said that a union representative told her that she should steer clear of CORE and Greenpeace, but he offered no further help from the union itself.

We eventually got Edward Clarke's case looked at again. The legal advice we received was that his cancer was probably not caused by his work on the AGR. He had only worked there for two years when he was diagnosed with his illness. However, we were the first people to have sought independent advice for Susan.

Susan knows that jobs depend on the plant. Her own father helped build it, both of her brothers-in-law work there and now her son and daughter do too. But she fears for the effect it has. 'There's so much illness around here. The man next door who worked with Eddy, he's died since of throat cancer, twelve months after Eddy. The man next door worked at Sellafield, he's dead with cancer in his mid-fifties too. I feel bitter with them now. Eddy died three years ago, but I don't think they even know I exist. I feel I've been treated badly by BNFL and I don't think they should have the authority to go and do what they want without asking permission.'

A letter to Susan Clarke from the Union's solicitors talks of the tests done by Schofield. 'The tests he (Schofield) carried out established to his satisfaction that the quantity of radioactive material present in your husband's prostate was infinitesimally small and did not contribute to the causation of the disease from which he died. He (Schofield) pointed out that prostatic cancers occur naturally in the male population and that there is no scientific literature establishing that such cancers might be caused by ionising radiation.'

Two years later a report by the Medical Research Council on the UKAEA workers at Dounreay was to show a high incidence of prostate cancers (ns 22.8.85). The men at Winfrith nuclear plant were nine times more likely to contract cancer of the prostate gland than members of a non-exposed workforce. This is thought to be linked to tritium exposure. Deaths from testicle cancer were more than twice the national average at Harwell, Culham and London research centres. Women in the five centres covered by the survey were nearly twice as likely to die from cancer of the uterus and the ovary.

Although Edward Clarke had been exposed to tritium, it is still held that his cancer was not due to exposure at Sellafield as the type of cancer he died from takes five to ten years to develop. As Susan Clarke rightly points out her husband probably had the disease when he started work for BNFL, which calls into question the effectiveness of their screening methods. Nor was it taken into account that Clarke had been on site at the time of the 1957 fire when the construction workers had no radiation-monitoring badges, even though it is possible some of them were quite badly contaminated by today's standards.

It is thought that radiation doses to construction workers were greatest at the time of the burst fuel releases. The radiation exposure for the population of Seascale is estimated to have been equal to or twice as high as the dose from the fire itself. No construction worker has ever brought a case against BNFL for his cancer, although over the years CORE has received many letters from the relatives of construction workers who died of cancer and were on the site in the 1950s.

CHAPTER

4

I know thee, solitary griefs, desolate passions, aching hours.
'The Precept of Silence', Lionel Johnson

Over the past ten years I have interviewed a number of widows of nuclear workers. The majority of those women never fully understood what kind of work their husbands did. It would also be fair to say that the majority never fully appreciated the dangers involved. Richard and Kay Appleton were an unusual couple in that they both started to work for Sellafield at the same time. They came back from working in Africa in 1974 and expected to find exciting new careers. However, for the first few months they both signed on the dole. Kay, a good-working woman now in her 38th year, recalls, 'Because we were living so close to Sellafield the Professional and Executive Register, which deals with graduates, sent both of us there for interviews. Needless to say we went with a lot of hesitation and a great deal of despair also. I cried in the lobby before we even got into Sellafield for the interview. I hoped we would fail the interviews. It was the beginning of 1975 and BNFL were desperate to take on anybody, especially graduates. We went in saying we knew nothing about the industry, we weren't even sure if we wanted to work for an industry like that. They took us both. Now in those days you had no choice. If you were offered a job like that at the right level you took it or you lost your dole.

'I had a degree in economics and Richard's was in chemical engineering. I didn't want to go in on the economics side. Because I was going to work there I wanted to be paid as well as I could and they paid more on the science side. So I went in on the science side. I had physics and chemistry and biology O-levels and so they were quite happy to take me, in fact they were overjoyed to have the pair of us. That is how we got started there, that was 1975. I was there for six years and Richard for five.'

Kay admits that her trepidation about working at the plant was linked to her ignorance of the industry. 'I was mostly frightened because I didn't understand it and didn't know anything about it. I wasn't sure if it would damage us or not. I suppose once I started work there I decided that really, as an industry, it is possible to run that industry safely. Having worked there a while I concentrated on that side of things. I made it quite clear that I wasn't happy with a lot of things that were going on. Mainly because the majority of the workforce there doesn't understand the safety side of things. Anyone who does not understand will not take enough care, even of themselves, and if they don't take care for themselves they are not taking care for the general public or the other people on the site.'

Kay and Richard soon moved to Waberthwaite, a small village eight miles south-east of Sellafield. The area is particularly beautiful, with the mountains providing a backdrop to fields, a river and a very contaminated Ravenglass estuary. Kay admits, 'I became incredibly aware of the environmental impact, particularly the discharges into the sea. As a worker in the industry I felt they were very wrong, very wrong indeed. Firstly I didn't like the idea of discharge anyway. There is no such thing as infinite dilution, not in a world that is as finite as ours is, you can't have infinite dilution. So to say you can filter it into the atmosphere and it will be infinitely diluted is rubbish. It doesn't matter if it is into the atmosphere or into the sea.

'The process workers who operated the sea-tanks came in during the night. They knew that if a sea-tank was there all day and the next day, that production had to slow down, which it did. It still should have stayed there because it wasn't fit to go out to sea within the limits we had then. Several of these process workers sent the sea tanks to sea in the night, on the night shift. We went into work the next morning and found they had gone and samples had gone. We didn't even know what radioactivity was in them. That was long before Greenpeace or anyone found out about them. Because I worked in the technical records office, I knew when things went into the sea and that was very worrying. I did that work because I was screened. I wasn't the only one in that office to raise complaints about this. To be fair the management were very, very upset about this at the time.

The trouble with the workforce there is that they are drawn from a very badly educated population. Cumbria has about the lowest record for education. Richard's father used to examine them for the Joint Matriculation Board and the record for Cumbrian schools is abysmal. It's sad, but it is the truth. The population of workers at Sellafield don't know what they are doing.

'As a member of staff Richard was not meant to be exposed to radiation, but I don't think that is necessarily true. They took on all these graduates in 1975 and didn't have anywhere to house them, basically. A lot of graduates were taken on to do research development and could have stayed outside of the active area completely. Or almost completely. A lot of them were housed in the active area. Which was a crazy way of operating. They put in an awful lot of Portakabins because they hadn't any proper blocks to put them in. These cabins were alongside a highly active pipe trench, which at that time was not capped. This was the pipe that came directly from the reprocessing plant into the silos. It was simply set into a concrete trench, there was nothing over it. Richard worked right next to that for a couple of years. During that time his film badge readings were more or less normal.

'Occasionally Rich came into contact with some high levels. We decided, because of where the cabin was in relation to the pipe trench, that any rays from the trench would hit the top section of the cabin and not the lower section at all. That is, they would be head high, or shoulder high. Maybe even chest high. A lot of the lads in those days, and Richard was no different from the rest, wore their film badges on their belts. Maybe that was a silly place to wear them. If he had worn it on his hat we might have had a better reading.

'Richard was taken ill in July 1977. We went on holiday in the July. We'd gone to London and he said he'd got a headache. We were planning on going across to Wales. London was very hot, so we put it down to the weather and the stress of driving. We decided we would clear off to Wales straight away. We got there, put the tent up and he said his headache was really bad. I was unhappy about this. Then he started being sick and that was very strange. So I said, well maybe we ought to go back home, if you really are feeling bad. Unlike him he agreed. Put everything back in the car. He got into the car and went unconscious. I drove back from Wales with him completely unconscious, he never spoke and he never moved. I got him home and a friend of ours who had been staying in our house helped me to get him into bed. The doctor came and the doctor said it was a dreadful migraine and left me on my own with him. By which time Rich went into a coma. I rang the doctor who didn't even come back to the house. I had to send for an ambulance which broke down. By now Richard was very dangerously ill indeed. They took him to hospital in Whitehaven about two in the morning, telling me he was going to die. I believed them, I was sure he would. I stayed until six in the morning and we decided that since he had survived that long they would try to take him across to Newcastle. When I got there I had to sign a form to say they could operate immediately. But he did survive it. At that point they didn't know what it was. They just thought it was some terrible blockage in the brain. It could have been a haemorrhage, they had no idea what it was.

'They kept him in hospital to do some tests. They obviously knew what his condition was then, but didn't tell us. Not for a while anyway. Then after about four weeks, when he was a lot better, they put a bypass in, around his brain and into his chest, so the fluid could drain away. He was looking like his ordinary self. He had no idea what was wrong with him. They told me that they thought he had cancer. They thought he was going to live for eighteen months, if that long. He was twenty-seven, the same age as me.

'I simply looked at him and thought, "You can't die." You don't believe you are going to die. Not when you have been fit and happy and well up to that time. I stuck with it and said don't tell him. He went to radiation treatment and the radiotherapist assumed he knew. The insensitive bastard. I didn't realise this chap had told him. We were going to walk back across the hospital together and he collapsed in the corridor. He said, "I'm going to die." We spoke to the specialist there who said there was a chance that he might not die. He realised Richard couldn't cope with it. He really couldn't help it. After about a year we thought he might not die, that there might be some remission. But with such a highly active tumour it was almost impossible that it could be controlled. Needless to say it just grew again. He didn't really ever realise, but I knew. They took him back into hospital and they said to me, we're going to tell him. They said, "We're going to keep him in, he's only going to live a few more weeks." I said you're not keeping him in. They can keep people in to make them healthy, but they can't keep them in to die. I took him home and he lived three months. He deteriorated, but he didn't really seem to grasp it, because it was his brain that was deteriorating. There were three days when he realised how bad he was getting, but it still didn't quite click. Then suddenly he was too far gone to even know.

'I can hardly describe it adequately now. I never could describe it altogether. I stopped eating. I think I've read about this – when someone is dying you stop wanting to eat. It was a form of anorexia in a way. I could feed him and I couldn't eat my own food. My memory was going wrong. I was getting thin. I just couldn't cope with him dying and me living. I just stopped eating and I started being sick. It made me physically sick in front of him.

'I was under terrible strain, I don't even want to think about it. My mum was a great help at this time. My family love me. In the end, when I said I took him home, I didn't take him home to Waberthwaite. I couldn't manage it physically. I took him over to my mum's and we stayed with my mum until he died. I don't think I could have managed all alone. I did everything really. We didn't have a nurse or anything. I nursed him, but I had done all the time. For two years, I did it all. I got used to it and in a way I was glad to do it. I wanted to do it and I didn't want somebody else doing it. I didn't want him to be in hospital. I hated it. They used to put up the sides of the bed, because he was losing his mind he would easily fall. I couldn't stand having him shoved in a bed with the sides around it. So, until he died, until the morning he died, I slept with him every night. The most frightening thing about it is he suffered a lot of pain, from the tumour growing. I would have liked to give him something to die. I didn't want him to live through that dreadful business. Yet I had to sort of keep him going, keep him alive, even when he was in all this pain.

'Strangely enough a lot of people I worked with felt a great deal, but most of them couldn't cope with it. I didn't see a lot of people from work while Richard was ill. Very few people actually visited him. Although his immediate bosses were very good to him and me. I don't know anyone else at Sellafield that was allowed to take the amount of time I took, seven months' unpaid leave – which they gave me without any trouble. When he was ill the last time, when he was dying, I said I just can't come in and they said we'll hold your job open as long as you like, whether it be a year or two years, whatever. In that sense they were quite caring, but people tended to avoid us, because it's not a happy business. I think it was more a social thing. They just couldn't cope with it. Just after he died they couldn't cope with me. It is difficult, I'm not sure I would be able to. I think now actually, I could, but unless you have been through it you don't cope with it very well. It is hard. So I never felt bitter about the fact that people did tend to avoid the issue.

'Richard had been there three years when his first symptoms came along. It happened very quickly. Which is why we associate it with Sellafield and not with a tumour that was growing a long time. It was a very fast-growing tumour. In fact when it was diagnosed it looked as if the damage was new. That is what we were told by the Royal Victoria Infirmary in Newcastle. I think people were very concerned as to whether it was Sellafield. I think the majority of the people I talked to tended to assume that it couldn't be Sellafield. But as I say, the staff there have a false loyalty. They didn't want to be caught out saying that Sellafield could ever be to blame. Once you start saying that you start questioning everything about the site and a lot of them have been there twenty or thirty years and didn't want to question anything.

'The staff union Richard was in was very, very unhelpful to me. Because really if I had taken any claim through the staff union it would have been against other members of the union. Sellafield is only the staff. That's all it is. The management of Sellafield is basically just the staff who work there. It wasn't just procedures laid down by management. It's hard to draw a dividing line once you get onto the management side. There's upper management, who give the actual regulations, but the others are only adequate while they are supervised well. It's very difficult for the management to supervise a workforce of 7,000 people, most of them unskilled, most uneducated. If there was any comeback it really does come down to a lot of middle management, rather than upper management who simply lay down the regulations and the rules. It's up to middle management to make sure they are carried out. Most middle management were our friends. I do firmly believe it was stupidity putting a lot of very young men in a cabin next to radioactive trenches. Not just radioactive trenches, but highly radioactive trenches.

'I think about the industry pretty much the way I thought about it ten or more years ago. That most industries can be run as safely as the people operating them know how. They still have a very poor workforce. They have men who knock pipes together and if this pipe doesn't fit that pipe they braid them until they do fit. Of course then you get cracks through the pipe and they don't supervise the welding correctly and they don't take shots of the welds and they don't check them. This pipework carries radioactive material which eventually seeps out.'

Early in 1988 four Sellafield blue collar workers came to CORE about a series of accidents at the plant. One of them told us, 'People who were working in the Active Workshop, if they were going to get a piece of equipment, just went in with their own work shoes on, bringing contamination back over the barrier to the monitor's office. If you went in the morning, you would see black tape on the floor where contamination was, and often there was a magic marker saying it was Grade 1 – five or six hundred counts per second. B314 Canteen is a case in point. It had holes or chalk marks on the carpet where contamination had been brought in from that area. So although you've got a monitoring system where realistically you're not supposed to be able to get through without putting your hands in the monitor and checking yourself, you can jump over the barrier. The people who are most guilty of not checking themselves are staff because they don't wear basic safety clothing, they wear their own clothing. When you come in on a morning you should totally change – underpants, vest, the lot. They don't, they just change their socks and put a white coat on so everything else is their own, so if they get any contamination they say nothing about it because they would have to throw away their own gear.

'You've got to discipline yourself to a certain extent, going into the active area. These people are normally in B403 administration: it's very rare that they come into an active area. They say "I'm not going to get changed into full basic clothing." The building could be contaminated from one end to the other but it wouldn't make any difference to them. Even the foremen don't wear basic clothing. It's status as well. At one time there were watches and weddding rings being taken away because they were contaminated. Until people got wise to it.'

But the men had a serious accident to tell us about, which happened in June 1987 during the annual shutdown. They believed the accident had not been fully reported to the Nuclear Installations Inspectorate, the organisation which oversees technical safety at nuclear sites. As one man explained, 'They knew for years that the old plutonium cells leaked along the pipe trench that was being renewed. When they had noticed that the plutonium had leaked its way to the surface they put four inches of concrete on top and sealed it with heavy duty lino. They kept it very, very quiet. In June they came to put the new pipe system in down the corridor in B205, to try and fall in line with the lower limits. It was also one of the older parts of the plant which needed changing anyway. They sent guys in with diamond drills and as soon as they drilled through the four inches of concrete a certain amount of airborne contamination was released. At the same time another team of men, at the other end of the corridor, breached a wall which had been put in to stop plutonium steam condensate leaking into the corridor. It had been leaking into the space behind the wall for years, it leaked all the time while we were trying to clean it. The press said BNFL were having a shutdown. It started off as a few days and then it went to two weeks and then months.

'They had never actually got to the root cause which was that plutonium was getting into a condensate tank which was filling up and finding its way, via the ventilation system, into tanks where it shouldn't have been going. This was getting into low-active tanks and then out to sea via B242 which did not have very good monitors then, although they've certainly improved now. Anyway, over a period of months various amounts of plutonium had been going down to sea and then they discovered what was happening. This was perhaps fifteen years ago.

'When they breached the wall the water came out as a flood and spread all the way down the corridor in B205 taking the plutonium with it. They kept paddling through and cross-contaminating everything in sight, and still drilling holes. Nobody was willing to say "Stop, we must stop and get this finished," even though alarms were going off. They stopped the work for a little while and sent the process workers in in Windscale suits with this "spill-sorb" stuff that absorbs liquid and they threw all that in. They must have shifted about a thousand bags of spill-sorb. They were taking it in in wheelbarrows, which had to be dumped in the end also.

'The pipe trench itself in some areas is two foot wide, some areas it goes down to about eighteen inches and it stretches from one end to the other of B205, which at the longest point is 250 metres, so you can say it stretched to 135, 140 metres and the whole lot of it was grossly contaminated because the water was allowed to swill right down to the far end. Certain areas were about a foot deep, but it slopes so there were areas where it was going to the top of your wellies. It was easy enough to actually stand in it and shovel it up and splash it about. It was serious contamination. They had to block the first floor off, seal the first floor stairs completely.

'Two men were put out of the area as a direct result of it. Somebody removed a Hoover from the corridor and brought it across a barrier. These two guys picked the hoover up and started hoovering the cell top and all the alarms went off in the cell top from one end to the other. The Hoover had plutonium in the bag but it didn't have the proper filtration system on it, which is part of the requirements for any Hoovering that's done on site.

'One of the guys was contaminated to such a level they were hesitating whether to give him the injection which helps to get the plutonium out of your body quickly. We've always been told that you must get it within the hour. This is what they told you in the plutonium course. But these guys didn't get it.

'The plutonium leakage should have been fixed long ago. Most of the managers in the building, apart from two, were actually in the building when it happened a long time ago, but nobody had the foresight to tell the drillers or to tell the Task Force what was there.

'Normally you're supposed to get a briefing to tell you what the hazards are, but nobody did on this occasion. Men were in Windscale suits on average four hours a day, sometimes longer. When it actually happened, the blokes that were doing the drilling, they were contaminated.

'On the monitor's report I saw the readings at the doorway, from samples they took, showed 3,000 counts per second right at the doorway. Counts per second is the actual measurement of atomic disintegration. Normally you'd expect a level of fifty or perhaps a hundred at the most. Then 5,000, 6,000 and there was a sort of platform where it was up to 17,000 counts per second. Everybody was expected to work four overtime shifts a week.

'They were all in Windscale suites because of the high levels of radioactivity in the dust in the corridor and in the air itself. So they had to feed air into the Windscale suites, but it was coming out on the last point along the air line. The air was travelling from the compressors all the way round B205 before it reached the men. Usually when you put men into a cell, you have maybe two, three at the most. They were putting seven and eight in, there just wasn't the amount of air necessary for that many men. The number of times men had to be cut out of Windscale suites because they didn't have enough air was too many! How somebody didn't die in that I really do not know.

'One guy in the corridor changing tent lost his air supply and he panicked. By the time he actually got to put his emergency breathing on it was too late. He was suffocating. The tents are usually dust mask areas but this one went above Windscale suit level so that meant the safety attendant couldn't help him. They have a button in there to get the monitor but he couldn't reach it so the attendant had to run to the door and start shouting, "Get somebody up here, this guy is in trouble!" He was in that bad a state the attendant had to go in the tent with a dust mask on and drag him out and get him out of that Windscale suit or he would have been dead. 'For that the attendant got a telling off. "He shouldn't have gone in there with a dust mask on."'

These workers also talked about the argument over the new dissolver for B205. The dissolver is the vessel in which the spent nuclear fuel rods are dissolved by nitric acid solution. Obviously such plant needs to be kept in tip-top condition as this is one of the most dangerous parts of the reprocessing cycle. Because the dissolver now in use was getting towards the end of its expected life the NII wanted a new, third dissolver built on the outside of B205. This would have cost £300 million. BNFL, on the other hand, believed they could safely take out the old dissolver and replace it and that would only cost £100 million. In the end BNFL put the new ventilation system on the exact spot where the NII had indicated they wanted the new dissolver to go.

On 29 July 1989 the *Whitehaven News* showed a picture of the B205 dissolver team that had taken this dissolver out. The next day BNFL admitted at a health conference that in 1988 500 men on site received a radiation dose over the 15mSv recommended level of exposure. Most of that would have come from decommissioning operations like taking out the old dissolver.

Because of the allegations made by these workers, we met with two NII inspectors and two of those making the complaints. I will call the two inspectors Brown and Green. Both men used to work for the nuclear industry. Brown told us that he had been surprised to arrive at Sellafield one Sunday evening to find men next to B205 laying foundations. When he asked what they were doing he could not get a straight answer. Green said that he would be putting something in his report about the dissolver, but nothing too heavy as, in his words, he had a wife and kids to think about as well.

On the issue of the corridor contamination Brown admitted that he had been into the B205 ground-floor corridor at the end of shutdown, therefore he would have seen only a minimal amount of dirt and mess. He admitted that there is a steel plate embedded in the floor of the ground-floor corridor warning people of the possibility of contamination. It says 'Danger greater than 3,000 c.p.s.'.

The men explained to the NII that they had not gone directly to them because they were worried about their jobs. The NII were concerned to hear of the amount of overtime being worked on site, as this could impair worker performance. The two workers described the different dodges used by workers to cover up badges to reduce the radiation exposure, but more worryingly they also explained how people can take other workers' badges and over-expose them in order to keep a worker out of the area (and possibly stop him from getting promotion).

Green admitted that like all people he knew the outcome of his actions and reports were coloured by what the political and personal consequences might be. He said that both he and Brown had the power to go and close Sellafield tomorrow – but the next day he knew he would be looking for another job. A very disconcerting confession to come from one of Britain's nuclear inspectors.

71

The NII admitted that they had only just begun to make impromptu visits to Sellafield. Prior to the allegations being made they had always given at least a day's notice to the plant that they would be arriving. The inspectors squirmed a bit when they heard the workers say that they, and everybody else on site, had always known of the NII's arrival in advance.

The men we spoke to were the first to acknowledge that not everybody ignored the safety rules. 'Mostly it's the guys who are not really interested. They're the dangerous ones, the ones who are only there for the money. Some do change their attitudes. There are foremen now who are getting early retirement, who have worked in B209 all their lives and have accepted all the shit over the years, because they're too scared to refuse. And the reward they get for faithful and unwavering loyalty for forty years is they're getting paid off early to let the young bucks come ahead. The people that were patting them on the back were the people that weren't exposing themselves. The new up and coming ones are being manipulated exactly the same way. They are getting rid of the old boys that have suddenly realised, "These buggers have been shitting on me for the last twenty years."

'I know someone who is going to church regularly, he goes to church every day now. He hasn't told his wife that he was put out of the area because he had reached the maximum saturation of plutonium in his body that's allowable. He's just told her that he's taking early retirement. This guy is running on his nerves now. He's noticed that the people who he has worked for, who were his bosses, who he emulated, are all "going missing in action".'

The men were quick to defend the majority of workers and the unions, who they believed tried very hard to make things work, but said that when the pressure was on certain of the workers overlooked safety practices. Nor are the workers unaware of what damage they might be doing to the environment.

'A lot of people now, the wives especially, have started to talk about it. You know, about kids going on to the beaches. People are becoming more aware that all the beaches are contaminated to a greater or lesser degree than is allowed inside the plant and a lot of the guys talk about it. You don't mention it when there's foremen or shift managers about but you do talk about it amongst yourselves. There's a greater awareness now about the ecological problems that the plant is causing. You do feel a bit guilty. I used to feel guilty. You know, I used to see people going on about it and I used to think "I'm part of this".'

CHAPTER

5

What is a man profited, if he shall gain the whole world, and lose his own soul?
Gospel According to Matthew

The unions at Sellafield have been caught up in the struggle between jobs and the environment, just like generations of workers before them. I well remember a conversation I had with Bill Robinson, the AEU convenor on site. Bill had been instrumental in organising an exhaustive tour around Sellafield in 1986 for CORE and Greenpeace. I do not think he expected us to come away praising the place, but he was obviously upset at what he saw as continuing attacks on the industry after he and other union men had gone to such trouble to show us the safety improvements they had fought for. Certain sections of the management have also made tremendous efforts to bring the new plant into line with better technology.

The day I saw Bill he was in no mood to hear our gloomy predictions of troubles yet to come. He told me he was annoyed at how we kept tying the industry in knots with issues such as the sea and air discharges. He could not see why we expected to have the right to know about every accident at Sellafield; next we would be saying there was a nuclear spill if a cleaner dropped a mop bucket.

He believed that if reprocessing were stopped, the plant would shut down entirely within five years. The plant was already facing lay-offs that year. Everybody would be on the scrap heap. I told him that Sellafield would have a lot of waste to deal with. Bill countered by saying that Sellafield can't keep on expanding and that they would not be given more space. He added that he did not see why Sellafield should 'take everybody else's shit' – a view hardly consistent with the fact that Sellafield's future in reprocessing depends on them taking foreign waste. Bill bemoaned the fact that because of the reduction in the amount of radioactivity discharged they now had to keep more waste at the plant and yet they have nowhere to put it. He said that there would be no trouble meeting the new lower radiation exposure levels on site, but that it was our fault that workers were getting exposed to more radiation because of our plans for storing waste above ground and because more waste was being kept on site instead of being dumped in the sea. He admitted that things such as the filters from SIXEP (the new waste treatment plant, Site Ion Exchange Plant) and the waste retained there all added to the problem.

Bill actually had the audacity to say that if there was a nuclear holocaust it would be because of us! He said that people within the plant could only take so much pressure and that good people would leave and that that would leave a bunch of cowboys.

At the time this conversation took place Bill Robinson was worried that the TUC would come out against reprocessing. He said that good workers were already starting to leave.

I was interested in Bill's view on worker health, but he would not be drawn. I asked him if he thought widows should know who decides on their claims. He refused to answer. He said that he thought BNFL did not send details out because the widows didn't want to know why their case had lost. I asked him if he had asked widows about this. He hadn't. He was happy with the scheme because people got paid and that is important.

I later found out that what had really been irking Bill Robinson was CORE's involvement with some of the worker cases. One of those cases was that of Phil Cundy who learnt the hard way that you do not speak to the press about Sellafield.

On the morning of 19 February 1986 Phil Cundy, a BNFL fitter, and three other men were working on a heat exchanger on No. 2 reactor at Calder Hall. The heat exchanger had been opened up for inspection for insurance purposes. Phil and his colleagues wore full PVC suits, wellington boots, dust masks and gloves for the work. The normal limit for this job was 0.4 mSv. The dictum at the plant is '0.4 no more', but in order 'to progress the job' a dose of 1 mSv was allowed with longer periods in-between. The job entailed going in at the top of the heat exchanger and coming out at the bottom. Here workers were undressed by a safety man. Phil's clothing had become covered in black dust (contaminated graphite particles) and as he stripped the dust flew about. Since he had been sweating, from working in a plastic suit, the loose dust readily stuck to his hair, throat, chest and face. On being monitored by a health physics monitor he was told to go and have a shower. The reading on Phil was 500 counts per second. The rule is you have to be down to five counts before you can go off the site. The initial shower did not clean Phil as well as intended and he was sent back for another shower before he came down to 'within limits'.

Phil was not happy and thought if the dust was loose on him he could have inhaled some. He complained to a union representative, who asked for a whole body monitor for Phil and the other two workers who had been contaminated. BNFL said they would get a full check when reactor No. 2 was brought up to power. They wanted Phil to be able to go on working on the job. As it happened Phil did not work on the heat exchanger again because he had reached 0.1 rem the first time on it. Instead he went on to general maintenance on other parts of the reactor.

Phil never did have a whole body monitor or nose swabs taken. His union representative did not follow it up. Had he been found to be contaminated due to lax working practices, he would have been put 'outside the area', but still on full pay, as the company has to bear responsibility in those cases. There is no doubt that practices were inadequate: as Phil pointed out, a hosing down of the suit before removal would have avoided contamination. In fact the practice that led to Phil being contaminated had gone on for twenty-five years, but was changed a short while after Phil spoke out. Phil has never had a copy of his radiation dose record for the time he worked for BNFL.

Phil told the story of his accident to the *Sunday Telegraph*, and it was easy to identify him from the article. The day after the story appeared in the newspaper Phil was ribbed by his workmates. He was later interviewed by a shop-floor manager and an engineer. They did not ask outright if Phil had spoken to the press, but did he think it was in the interests of the company and the workmen when journalists wrote articles such as the one which had appeared in the *Sunday Telegraph*? One of those present said, 'Do you realise the Labour Party want to shut this place down and you're giving them ammunition.' Over the next few days a number of jokes were made. Phil, who had a Greenpeace sticker on his car, saw a Greenpeace application form on a notice board. Phil even played along with the joke, telling his workmates that he'd collect their Greenpeace application forms. Some of the managers said 'Don't speak to him, he's a mole'. The accident in which Phil was contaminated occurred during the highly publicised spate of accidents in 1986. The incident was never publicly reported by the company. When a call was made by a newspaper to a call box outside health physics at Calder it was suggested that Phil had been giving information from this call box to the local media. Later it became known that it was someone from the administration building who was leaking information to the press.

However, Phil Cundy was obviously going to be made the scapegoat. He was asked to resign. It was said he was a Greenpeace member and management were unhappy because Phil had privately voiced his disquiet over the level of sea discharges and the military contract of the Calder Reactors.

On 13th March Phil was fired. He had never been a member of Greenpeace or CORE. At the time of his sacking neither organisation knew of him. At the initial hearing when Phil was sacked management repeated verbatim jokes that had been made by Phil to his workmates. Notes had obviously been taken of what he had said in jest. When the Appeals Committee failed, Phil asked his union for help to pursue a claim for unfair dismissal. They said they could not help him with legal representation, although a union official would help him at the hearing. At this point Phil decided to turn to CORE for assistance and Geoff Clapp, a Carlisle solicitor, won Phil a £6,000 award two days prior to a scheduled full and public hearing for unfair dismissal.

In a statement made by the company when Phil was fired, BNFL said the reason for sacking Phil was that 'he failed to cooperate in a preliminary hearing'. The company rules, which forbid workers to talk about their work to outside agencies, are specifically designed to stifle any open debate. When the new Chairman of BNFL, Christopher Harding, took office in April 1986, he promised an open industry. Reacting to criticism of a closed and secretive industry he wrote, 'BNFL will seek to refute that criticism by demonstrating a frank and open policy, welcoming visitors to its plants and responding freely to all requests for information except where the dictates of national security, commercial confidentiality and personal privacy impose restraints.' (obs 6.4.86). Yet strict rules about who workers could speak to were reissued only two months after Harding's arrival in July 1986. Those rules, which still apply, are as follows:

a) Employees are reminded of the Official Secrets Act, and they are bound by the Secrets Act after leaving the company's employ. Incidents appearing to indicate a breach of 'fidelity' or of the Official Secrets Act must be reported. b) Employees are forbidden to communicate any information obtained in the course of their employment to any person without proper authority, or give such information to any newspaper or publish any material or take part in any broadcast on any matter relating to their employment without prior consent in writing of the general manager or superintendent. c) Employees are not permitted to accept invitations to appear as expert witnesses in private lawsuits for the purpose of giving evidence on matters of which they have acquired knowledge in the course of, and in connection with, their employment. If, after replying to such a request that company regulations do not allow them to give evidence, they are subpoenaed to appear as expert witnesses, the matter should be reported at once to the General Manager or superintendent.

The fear created by people speaking out arises partly because the Sellafield union attitude reflects the mentality of an isolated and closed community. There is a belief that if you speak out you not only risk jobs, but also that it breaks an unwritten code not to criticise 'your own' in public. My own mother always hammered home the point to us that we should look after our own and that family rows were done behind closed doors. On a bigger scale the local men who represent the unions still carry on with this attitude.

There are those Cumbrians though who, whilst understanding the problems of the area, also believe that the unions could do more. Maurice Telford is one such man. Born in 1918, his father was a pit man who was active in the Independent Labour Party. Maurice himself started in a pit at sixteen, then he was a gardener and a construction worker. He was called up in 1940 and served in France with the Royal Engineers. He returned home in 1946 and settled at Lorton. He went to teacher training college at Lancaster then taught at Whitehaven and Workington. He married in November 1949. His wife, Barbara, died of cancer in 1983, aged sixty-three.

Maurice understands all too well the pressures on the men who had come through the 1930s: the very same men who first worked at Sellafield and whose memories haunt their sons. 'People are poor now who are on benefits, but nothing like the poverty of that time. There is no starvation, you don't see hundreds of tramps on the roads, people begging for bread. Any hope of employment, especially skilled work, was marvellous. The depression hit West Cumbria far harder than even places like Jarrow. Maryport had the highest unemployment rate in the 1930s – 80 per cent! The long hardships and the war certainly took their toll on people. West Cumbria was in decline from the beginning of the century. It was very difficult to equate the risk of a job with the gain of the job, everybody worked in harsh conditions. Hundreds died in the pits in Cumbria. Death and injury were no strangers, and neither was pollution. However, everybody knew how coal-mines affected the workforce, but that's not so with nuclear plants.

'I feel Sellafield trade unions have been sucked into a situation from which they can't recover. If trade unions would think more in terms of what's going to happen to their grandchildren instead of what's going to happen next week, I think they'd be more honoured by members and the public. I don't think it's anything to condemn or defend because it's something over which they have no control. It's of international import, it's part of western strategy and nuclear power in its political sense, it's got to be there as long as this present policy continues. It will take a political decision to alter it, although I think people can act to help change things. Sadly I don't think trade unions in this area have the strength to push away from Sellafield.

'As someone who is from a working class background, I believe we have a duty to work and act for ourselves. We've offered a high level of education to people and it's one thing I can't forgive about trade unions and working people. They've rejected education and I had to fight for that. Their level of culture, of understanding, of intelligence, has been impaired and that's not been forced on them, that's their own choice. They don't have to buy the *Sun* or listen to rubbish on the TV or radio. In Dearham records show 200 to 300 people attending evening classes years ago, not just yoga or flower arranging, but mathematics, philosophy, the classics. People studied, they read. They understood and were able to understand and interpret, but I'm afraid not now, it hasn't had any impact even with all this mass of information.'

Maurice's view is in direct contradiction to that of Bill Maxwell, the most outstanding and well-known trade unionist at Sellafield. For many years Bill was the chief convenor for the General Municipal and Boilermakers trade union (GMB) and during that time he played an important role in West Cumbria and Sellafield's future. Bill believes that the plant is a safe place to work and that it is good to see the nuclear industry expand. Bill also knew what poverty could do to people. Born and bred in Cleator Moor, he was able to recount the tales from the coal mines as good reasons why Sellafield should not only be built, but helped to grow.

When the Thermal Oxide Reprocessing Plant (THORP), the second generation of reprocessing plant, was first mooted, Bill was quick to urge people to accept the idea. He told his union's annual conference in 1976 that to ban importing nuclear waste would, 'deny us the lucrative profits which would help this country's balance of payments problem. Rest assured, if we don't snap up the contracts from abroad, France, Sweden or some other country will. I resent the implication that Windscale is an atomic dustbin spilling radioactivity into the atmosphere and sea. Windscale is very much a controlled and contained environment and I can assure you that to the best of my knowledge and belief, workers apart, no hurt or harm has been caused to any person, animal or marine life outside the plant. Do you seriously believe we would expose our children, our families and ourselves to danger?' (w/n 16.6.76 and e/m June 76).

Bill's argument, that people would not live near or work in an unsafe industry is not one that holds water, although it is all too easy to believe that workers living near a plant make for some sort of mystical guarantee. The unions went so far as to put this claim in writing in a 1989 submission to the Labour Party 'the organised workforce is itself a genuine guarantee that the industry will maintain its fine health and safety record'. He knew that there were many people worried about THORP, not least because the plant would take oxide spent fuel, which is ten times hotter and more radioactive than magnox fuel. At that time French nuclear workers at the Cap de la Hague reprocessing plant were on strike over safety and security fears concerning oxide reprocessing.

BNFL's experiments with oxide fuel in the early 1970s had led to a major blow back accident (see chronology) which seriously contaminated thirty-five men and closed for ever the B204 reprocessing plant. THORP was also to take overseas spent fuel and it was feared that this would make Cumbria the world's dumping ground. Of the 6,000 tonnes to be reprocessed in the first ten years, two-thirds was intended to be British and one-third foreign (a situation now in fact reversed). Although this was such an important step forward in nuclear power in Britain there were many who did not want to see any inquiry at all. Bill had the workers organise a petition to call for the expansion of the plant, which got 18,000 signatures compared with 26,000 from local anti-nuclear protesters calling for an inquiry.

Because people like Bill Maxwell are decent family men, it is difficult to think they might do anything that would harm people. But the workers at Flixborough, Bhopal, Seveso, Chernobyl and scores of other places were no different. They were probably no less caring, yet either deliberately or unwittingly they did put themselves and others at risk. Even the coal miners at Aberfan played a part in resisting moves to have the slag heap made safer. They feared money put into that might make the mine less profitable.

In 1976 the threats about jobs were coming in thick and fast. In December BNFL director Con Allday said: 'If we have to go through the delays of a public inquiry I believe that all the overseas reprocessing business we are presently negotiating . . . will be lost.' (w/n 16.12.76). At a public meeting held prior to the inquiry Peter Mummery, then plant manager, said that if the expansion did not go ahead, three-quarters of the plant would have to shut down with a loss of 3,000 jobs.

Bill Maxwell had some very well placed allies, notably in Dr John Cunningham, the Copeland MP and Labour environment spokesman. Cunningham is, in fact, sponsored by the largest union at Sellafield, the General Municipal and Boilermakers. Cunningham had quickly made the right contacts in Westminster, becoming Parliamentary Private Secretary for Jim Callaghan and then a Minister to Tony Benn's Secretary of State for Energy. Cunningham held this position at the time of the Windscale Inquiry. It was an opportunity for him to flex his political muscles.

He told the Commons during the debate on the proposal to build THORP, in January 1976, that 'the community seems to be overwhelmingly in favour. These people live there, they bring their children into the world less than five miles from BNFL. There is tremendous competition to get employment at Windscale. I regard it as totally unsatisfactory to suggest that local men and women would take working conditions and safety lightly. This goes against all trade union traditions of the people.' (e/m 16.1.76). Over the years the local Labour Party has constantly backed an expansionist policy for Sellafield and Jack Cunningham has always fought for that in the Commons and the party itself. In 1982 he pointed out that all nuclear power stations ordered since 1960 had been ordered by Labour Governments. Indeed, the Labour Party has very much supported nuclear power in the past and even people like Tony Benn have been in favour.

Benn's faith in the industry was to be soured when details of one of the worst known leaks at Sellafield emerged in December 1976. The leak had happened in B38, a silo which contained a type of high level liquid waste. The leak had occurred because the silo had only a single wall which had failed to contain it. The story became public when a Scottish MP, James Dempsey, was told by some of his constituents who had been on holiday in Cumbria that Sellafield workers had told them that there was a 'no-go' area inside the plant. Dempsey tabled a question in the House. Tony Benn, then Energy Minister, was forced to admit that Dempsey's query was the first he had heard of it (sunday sun 12.12.76). Benn said that 'There is no evidence of contamination from this leak reaching groundwater, nor has the leak caused any contamination of surface water.' On the same day Benn had to admit that tritium was found on the beach at Sellafield and that it could be linked to the silo leakage. Benn said, 'I am advised that the tritium level on the beach is well below that which is permissible in drinking water and constitutes no hazard to employees or the general public.' (e/m 16.12.76). Benn had no idea of how serious the leak was because BNFL reports to the Department of Industry, which tells the Department of Energy of accidents only if it sees fit. The leaking silo was only 200 yards from the River Calder where farmers took their cows to drink.

At the same time, BNFL admitted that up to 100 gallons of

contaminated water a day had leaked from the 70,000 gallon silo. It was believed the silo had been leaking since the early 1960s. John Doran, the assistant general manager, told reporters, 'We already have a trench cleared to twenty feet along the north wall. It could be coming out now or it could have sealed itself – leaks often do!' (w/n 12.12.76). It was not BNFL's monitoring which brought the problem to light, but a torrential rainstorm which brought radioactivity to the surface. The leak was ten feet below ground.

That leaking silo had been discovered on 12th October. The County Council Planning Committee gave the go-ahead for the new THORP plant on 2nd November. The authorities denied covering-up the leak whilst the decision on THORP was being made. The leak also came two weeks before Peter Shore was to give his blessing to THORP, or call for an inquiry. Although the unions had not been officially informed of the leak they were not worried. Bill Maxwell said the fact that tritium had been found on the beach 'will have the desirable effect of educating the public. This cannot but do good, because once people have eliminated the fear of the unknown they will appreciate the marvellous advances of British science and technology and indeed the wonders of Windscale. We in this industry have a wonderful opportunity to earn much needed foreign currency.'

The inquiry when it did happen proved to be something of a landmark, and the forerunner of the inquiries into the Sizewell B and Hinkley C pressurised water reactors.

Joe Thompson was one of the people who got the inquiry off the ground. 'When it became obvious that there might, or might not be, an inquiry into the building of THORP a few of us set ourselves up in a little group called the Network for Nuclear Concern. There was a big public meeting in Whitehaven held by the County Council. There were a lot of BNFL trade unionists there and one of them stood up half way through the meeting and shouted, "it's no good coming here blinding us with facts". I always remember that. After that public meeting it was actually said in the House of Commons that that public meeting had been wholeheartedly in support of the expansion of Windscale, but it hadn't been.'

Joe was worried at the level of ignorance there was about the actual importance of THORP. 'There was an interesting interview done by the *Newcastle Journal* in which they interviewed the local planning committee. Not one of them knew the difference between oxide and magnox fuel. Several of them are quoted as saying they did not know what it was all about, but they were determined to get the number of jobs sorted out.'

Joe Thompson was not a political person and his foray into the Inquiry system came as something of a shock to him. He recalls, 'They tried to block Radford, one of our chief witnesses, coming here. The Embassy, the US rather than the UK Embassy, in Washington wrote to the National Academy of Sciences and tried to get Radford stopped. It became quite fierce. In the end Radford had to say he was going to resign, and that he was going over to the Windscale Inquiry. Another chap we wanted, Rowe of the EPA, that was definitely stopped. Rowe was actually told by the US authorities that he was not to go.'

Of course the arguments put forward did nothing to stop THORP getting the go-ahead. Only one County Councillor spoke out. The Conservative Raven Frankland, said, 'West Cumbria has had a shabby deal for a long time and now is negotiating from a position of weakness – having to take the things nobody else wants. If this thing is so glamorous and safe, London would have bagged it.' (w/n 4.11.76).

It is now twelve years since THORP was given the go-ahead and the project is still the subject of much debate. One of the major environmental problems involved with reprocessing is Sellafield's role as a creator of nuclear waste. This matter was raised in 1986, by the Conservative-dominated House of Commons Environment Committee. The Committee, chaired by Sir Hugh Rossi, had been given the remit to look at nuclear waste. As a reprocessing plant Sellafield creates the largest amount, in terms of bulk, of nuclear waste of any facility in the UK. The final report was 'sanitised' for public consumption. Damaging references to the nuclear industry being 'virtually light years' behind other countries and disposal sites being 'primitive in the extreme' had been removed from the preface to the report (g. 22.1.86).

However, that report still carried one major recommendation: that the Department of Energy and BNFL should undertake an economic review of THORP. If too much money had not already been sunk into the project then the possibility of abandoning the idea should be looked at. Obviously the Committee was looking for some way out of the morass that reprocessing had got Britain into. Spent fuel reprocessing is like some perverted Midas touch in that everything turns into nuclear waste. In bulk terms reprocessing creates two hundred times more nuclear waste than is originally put into the system. The Environment Committee believed that if THORP could be stopped we would break the vicious circle of nuclear waste creation.

However, the Department of Energy and BNFL had no inclination to review the economics of THORP and simply refused to comply with the recommendation. They tried to stick with the main argument that they favoured reprocessing as it is good waste management. They have said it is better to reprocess spent fuel and return the plutonium and uranium to the fuel cycle and leave behind a small amount of high level waste to be dealt with.

This in itself is a fairy tale. Everyone within the industry knows that for many years the price of uranium has not actually justified reprocessing. Of approximately 30,000 tonnes that has gone through the present magnox reprocessing plant only 840 tonnes has been recycled. It is cheaper to use fresh uranium straight from the mines. Also uranium which has been through a reactor is 'contaminated' with other uranium isotopes and during the process of cleaning recycled uranium environmental discharges are increased. This process also needs fresh uranium to be put in with the old material to give a boost so it is rich enough to work in a generating plant. Plutonium, the second great reason for reprocessing, now no longer has a commercial value as the Dounreay Fast Breeder reactor programme has been abandoned by the government. The only use now left for the plutonium is to go into British nuclear weapons or be sent to the US for use in their nuclear arms.

Jack Cunningham told the local Labour Party, 'What we cannot accept and what I reject is the suggestion that the people of this area should pay for errors of management and the failures of government policy with their jobs.' Of course, it was Cunningham's government in 1976 which led the Copeland area ever further into the nuclear morass. Cunningham went on, 'It is unacceptable to us that the environment can only be protected at the cost of employment. It is unacceptable for people in other parts of the country to indulge themselves and their views at the cost of working people in West Cumbria.' (w/n 20.3.86). As an MP Cunningham was simply looking after what he believed to be the best interests of his constituency. Although who would now say that nuclear reprocessing plants are a good thing for anyone apart from BNFL?

The cost of THORP has risen from £350 million to £1.85 billion and it will now have to reprocess an extra 1,000 tonnes of Japanese waste to pay for the increase. Between 1977 and 1985 BNFL received £136.1 million, or 77 per cent of all the regional development grants for West Cumbria. In Copeland, BNFL's gross share of these grants rose from 63 per cent in 1977 to 94 per cent in 1984. These huge grants were given out on the basis that many jobs would result from the investment. However, those jobs were to cost the UK taxpayer dearly. The average grant-aided job at Sellafield cost £65,000, compared to £23,000 in the most hi-tech jobs in the oil industry and only £3,000 to £5,000 in light engineering. All the local politicians condemned the loss of grant status and bemoaned the fact that they would now be even more dependent on BNFL. At the same time Rowntree closed its Egremont factory because, it is believed, it did not want its product associated with Sellafield. That led to fifty jobs lost.

In September 1985 the European Parliament passed a resolution in which it 'calls upon the Commission to examine the scope for intensive European Community participation in the creation of alternative, acceptable employment in the Cumbria area to provide work for the existing workforce and those dependent upon operations at Windscale to avoid any addition to the already high level of unemployment should closure prove necessary.' Because that same resolution called for the closure of Sellafield the unions and BNFL management chose to ignore it. Within the last year Copeland has gone begging to the EEC to ask if they will consider giving special aid to the area because of the impending 4,500 redundancies from the site. When those job losses come, unemployment in the district could rise by 200 per cent by the mid-1990s.

Party politics have played a significant role in Sellafield's history. For a number of years some people within the Labour Party have expressed concern at what they consider to be a conflict of interests between Jack Cunningham's link with Copeland industry and his role as the then Shadow environment secretary. Not only is he a great supporter of BNFL, but he is also an industrial consultant to Albright and Wilson who own Marchon, a detergents factory which overlooks (and overshadows) Whitehaven. Marchon has been cited as the UK's largest discharger of cadmium, a toxic heavy metal. In fact there have been a number of environmental problems associated with the company. Neil Kinnock has already shown his support for Cunningham. He wrote, 'He has my complete confidence and his general abilities are in my view enhanced by his long history of efforts to secure significant improvements in nuclear energy policy and provision.'

1986 brought a battle over nuclear power between the Labour Party and various trade unions – both for and against it. Even before the Chernobyl disaster a large number of anti-nuclear resolutions had been put forward at that year's Labour Party conferences. In fact to this day the record for the largest number of resolutions on any single topic in one year is for those to get rid of nuclear power. Cunningham was in a fighting mood. 'There have been some discussions about nuclear power since Chernobyl, but it is definitely not Labour Party policy to abandon THORP. The project was agreed by the Labour Government. It is unthinkable that a Labour Government would make decisions to put thousands of people out of work.' Cunningham was speaking after Copeland councillors and union leaders had visited Kinnock to plead for their corner. The leader of the local Copeland Labour Group, Councillor Jimmy Johnston (BNFL Suggestions Manager) said, 'We want to give Mr Kinnock our point of view. It was not for him to give any answers. This area is supportive of the BNFL operation and we wanted to make that clear. He said he would take our points into consideration.' (w/n 31.7.86).

However, immediately after the Environment Committee's report, Copeland Council had issued a joint statement, with Jimmy Johnston, which read, 'It is not for us to comment on what should or should not be carried out at Sellafield so long as it does not affect the environment or the people of this area in physical terms or damage the economic health of the area.' Commenting on the suggested financial appraisal of abandoning THORP the statement said: 'If this is relating to the financial issues only then we cannot take exception to that recommendation. Our concern is not to support THORP as such, but to ensure the economic health and survival of this area and its people. To date we have no cause to be over-concerned about the effect of BNFL operations on the people or the environment. We have been and continue to be concerned about the way this area is now seen because of BNFL's presence. What we want are jobs – and if these jobs are in making biscuits, shoes or cars, rather than reprocessing nuclear fuel, so be it. It's OK with us.' (w/n 13.3.86).

Fearful of a Labour Party vote to close Sellafield, the unions mounted a campaign to challenge the Party. The National Campaign for the Nuclear Industry was created by the on-site unions and collected money for its publicity. On April 14th, five days before Chernobyl, the TUC review committee on nuclear power visited Sellafield. The same week Cunningham attacked moves by Party activists to stop nuclear power: 'Too often anti-nuclear activists inside and outside the Labour Party demonstrate little knowledge of the nuclear industry. Too often they seem careless of those thousands of workers and their families dependent on the industry.' (w/n 24.4.86). Unfortunately Cunningham had just written an article for the April edition of the Labour Party paper Tribune in which he wrote, 'All major industrial competitors are proceeding with and developing their nuclear power generation.' (w/n 18.4.86). Chernobyl put a stop to the claim. By May of 1986 Cunningham had signed the Labour Party policy document, along with the rest of the Shadow Cabinet, which agreed to phase out nuclear power. The statement 'supports the recommendations of the Environment Select Committee for an economic reappraisal of the THORP plant at Sellafield.' They also signed saying 'any additional generating capacity will be met by ordering coal-fired power stations. Wherever appropriate combined heat and power systems will be built. Energy conservation will be a priority. As part of a programme to eliminate fuel poverty and promote the efficient use of fuel we will launch a major energy conservation programme.' (w/n 21.5.86).

However, in August 1986 the NEC of the Labour Party decided not to vote to scrap THORP and Cunningham claimed a victory. He criticised other NEC members by saying some of them, 'have little understanding or care for the people of West Cumbria and were determined to commit Labour to abandon THORP.

Thankfully the NEC came to the realisation it could not write off the future of the business and so many jobs.' (w/n 7.8.86). The Labour Party motion that was eventually agreed did not call for the immediate phasing out of nuclear power by a Labour Government, but still committed the Party to the completion, but not the use, of THORP. The union policy towards nuclear power is, in itself, confusing. The GMB is, on paper, opposed to building Pressurised Water Reactors (of the type which went so disastrously wrong at Three Mile Island). Yet in order to support a plant like THORP into the next century BNFL first needs the fuel from PWRs.

The local Conservatives were not to be left out. Early in 1986 a local organisation, the 'Friends of Sellafield', had been formed. The chairman was Rex Toft, a Conservative County Councillor who, at that time, was also the prospective Parliamentary candidate for the Tories in Copeland. Jack Cunningham had agreed to be the President of the 'Friends'. The aim of the group was to defend Sellafield against misrepresentation by the environmental lobby. To give an idea of the tone of the meeting, a banner across the front of the platform read 'Save Sellafield. Shut Greenpeace'. About 300 people attended the first meeting. A message from Jack Cunningham said that pressure groups' closure calls were 'facile and based on anti-technology, anti-industry naïvety'. Both the SDP and Liberal Parties in Copeland welcomed the forming of the group (w/n April 1986).

At the next meeting of the Friends, in July of 1986, only twenty people turned up. Rex Toft said that there had been a reluctance among Sellafield workers to join the Friends or even sign a petition supporting the industry. 'There is a strong feeling among the workforce that it's not for them to join the Society, it's for people who don't work here. They feel they may be prejudiced because of financial incentive.' Toft added that he thought the low turnout was due to confidence rather than lack of interest. 'The fact that there are so few people here is a sign of confidence because most people get het up when they are worried. Maybe complacency is part of it, but if a large number of people felt Sellafield was a serious risk to their health they would be here asking questions.' The meeting was supported by Tony Hildrop, Copeland Labour county councillor and chair of the Cumbria tourist board (w/n 10.7.86). Toft omitted to mention the accident at Chernobyl which had happened only some three months before.

Toft's and Cunningham's collaboration in the Friends of Sellafield did not stop the Tories from using the Labour Party Conference vote to claim that jobs were safe only with them. Rex Toft said: 'The vote at the conference has now made it clear that the Labour Party intends to shut down Sellafield. Anyone who saw on television the cheers and applause for those speakers who want to close down the nuclear industry and the open hostility shown to those speakers who supported it can be in no doubt about that. The fact that there is dispute among Labour supporters over how rapidly the phasing out process proceeds will be no comfort to West Cumbria. The only way to protect thousands of jobs in Copeland is to see to it that there is not another Labour Government. In my opinion Copeland will elect a Conservative member of Parliament at the next election. The Copeland electorate really has no option if it is to prevent the area becoming an economic wilderness. I realise that many habitual Labour voters will face what for them is a dilemma, with a heavy heart. The pull of party loyalty is strong, but loyalty runs two ways. The fact is that the Labour Party has now betrayed the loyalty of thousands of its supporters in West Cumbria (w/n 9.10.86). Cunningham was re-elected in the 1987 general election.

When the four proposed Southern dump sites were abandoned in April 1987, BNFL denied any such plans to have the dump at Sellafield instead. In September 1987 BNFL announced the proposal to have an undersea dump. At the press conference with BNFL company secretary Harold Boulter were Jack Cunningham and Jimmy Johnston. Selected members of the Liaison Committee had also had discussions at Sella Park, the company's 'guest house'. In fact those secret discussions would never have become public knowledge had an unwitting County Council official not noted the meeting in the minutes of the County Council itself.

Not all the politicians in West Cumbria see eye to eye with BNFL. Marjorie Higham, councillor for the area which covers the Drigg nuclear dump, is an ex-Sellafield worker who is less than enthused by the plant now. Although she was one of the people who came to Cumbria to set up the industry, she now sees things differently. 'I wish they'd stop reprocessing. I've wanted them to stop since the 1977 Inquiry into THORP. The oxide fuel, it seems absolutely ludicrous to dissolve that up and then turn the fission products into glass blocks. It seems absolutely barmy. I didn't want them to start with THORP until they had sorted the waste thing, and now here they are ten years later no better off. And we're still no further forward with ten years' more rubbish. Technically it wasn't necessary and if they had put the technology and money in the right place it needn't have happened. I just want to make sure that they never do it again.'

But Les Tuley, the head of Information Services at Sellafield, told me he believes reprocessing is the best way of dealing with nuclear waste and is good for Britain. 'The go-ahead for THORP meant that apart from our own oxide fuel we could do business with overseas. The cost of building these plants is very, very large indeed. From the UK's point of view if we can get overseas customers to pay for part of that plant, then that is a good thing. Otherwise it means that our own home boards, the CEGB, would have to pay for the whole cost which would certainly make the cost of electricity dearer. So there is an economic benefit. We are the largest Japanese yen earner in the country. Given the reputation of the Japanese for not importing things into their country I think that is quite an achievement.'

Les is also keen to point out that the plant provides jobs in other places. 'Apart from sustaining the nuclear power stations, these new projects require building and equipment – in some cases extremely advanced technological equipment. This is keeping many industries going, particularly the steel industry. I think we take something like a quarter of the special steels division of British Steel. Of course there is all the electronics, the computers and this kind of thing. Over a hundred thousand jobs outside the nuclear industry are sustained by the new projects like the ones I've mentioned. Of course we buy in other things like food. This is where the little firms could be set up to make these things, which could live off the demand from a place as big as this and then may well expand. For transporting the spent fuel to Sellafield, British Rail gets about five million.'

A number of countries have now abandoned or rejected the idea of reprocessing spent nuclear fuel. The US closed its West Valley oxide plant as it was neither 'technically nor economically feasible'. Les Tuley stands by the viewpoint that it is, in fact, the best thing to do with the waste. 'Some people say that you should just store the fuel and dispose of it in engineered storage. If you reprocess you can recycle most of the fuel and the very fact that you separate the waste from the plutonium and from the uranium means that you can then package each item specifically and in a far better way than if you package the lot together. The highly radioactive waste you separate can then be put into a form which is safest for that particular type of waste. The plutonium can be stored in the best conditions of storage for plutonium. It can be used again and recycled and eventually ends up as waste. By reprocessing you get a much more satisfactory way of storing each component. Most of it, the uranium, is not particularly radioactive and can be stored in an ordinary drum, so 99 per cent of it is actually taken out and does not need any special storage. That in itself is a plus factor in favour of reprocessing. The other benefit is that you can use 99 per cent of it, particularly in the magnox. The same arguments go for the oxide fuel. If you don't reprocess you've still got to spend all this money looking at suitable means of storing it.'

Of course the pro-nuclear lobby does not draw attention to the fact that reprocessing does not decrease the amount of radioactivity that has to be dealt with, but simply spreads it around.

Les Tuley believes Sellafield would be the best resting place for most of Britain's nuclear waste. 'Sellafield is a reprocessing factory and with reprocessing you have got to handle waste. If we are looking for somewhere to put waste in its final resting place, being realistic, political opposition and the public's perception of this, it's going to be very, very difficult for any Government to get a site accepted by the people of that area. In the end Sellafield is going to have to demonstrate that having a waste repository either on the site or under the site or under the sea is safe.

'If we can prove that you can have a repository and that it is safe then I think that there is a chance that other areas may then say, oh well, it's proved to be safe so possibly we will accept it. I can very well understand the local people round here who say, why should we have all the waste if the rest of the country isn't going to share it? They are almost bound to take the attitude of well, if we are going to take it there should be some benefit from it. I see Sellafield as being the centre of excellence in dealing with this waste and demonstrating that we can deal with it at all levels quite safely and we can demonstrate that it can be stored safely.'

Other promises have been made about the possible benefits of the dump. In November of 1983, Copeland Council voted to reject the applications for THORP and the high-level waste storage plant until they had extracted from the Government promises regarding the Egremont bypass (a much needed local road, especially because of BNFL's increased traffic). They were told that work would start in 1987. It still hasn't started. However, BNFL have managed to have built, at a cost of £5.5 million, an improved road from the plant to the main A595.

The Council has, in its turn, been pressurised by BNFL. In 1985 the Council granted BNFL storage space for only 5,500 cubic metres of intermediate-level nuclear waste at the site, one-sixth of the amount BNFL had asked for. The Council felt that by restricting space they would make sure foreign waste went back and also that the Nuclear Industry Radioactive Waste Executive would hurry up and find a suitable dump site. Jimmy Johnston said, 'We are of the opinion that Windscale is not appropriate for long term storage of intermediate waste and the amount of storage we have allowed gives the appropriate agencies sufficient time to identify final depositories.' But in 1988 BNFL and NIREX were nowhere nearer to finding a nuclear waste dump for low- and intermediate-level waste, having been chased off every other site in the country. They still had to find room for their nuclear waste. In July 1988 a proposal to allow BNFL 18,000 cubic metres of storage space for intermediate-level waste was put before the full Council. After very little dissent it was given the go-ahead. What must have weighed heavily on the Councillors' minds that day was a press release which had gone out from the company two days earlier in which BNFL claimed that reprocessing at Sellafield would stop by 1995 if they were not given clearance to go ahead. BNFL had the audacity to say that part of the reason for the urgency of the decision was the fact that sea discharge reduction technology meant that they now had more nuclear waste on site and this was leading to problems! (e/m 2.7.88).

The Advisory Committee on the Safety of Nuclear Installations had reported in June 1987 that keeping more waste on site was a problem because of reduced environmental discharges and could also increase the risk of accidental releases (tel 23.6.87). BNFL denied this (w/n 25.6.87).

Despite the fact that privatisation is now weighing heavily against the industry, Les Tuley, ever the optimist, still sees a bright future for it. 'I can see THORP number two being built. Being political, I can see that unless the public perception changes then they would have difficulty building it anywhere else than at Sellafield or at some nuclear site where the local population accepts nuclear operations. Into the next century there would be need for it. The present one will deal with anything we've got. The first ten years are booked up and the second ten years are available. It does depend on how the nuclear industry develops. Chernobyl has made people stop, pause and think. There are all kinds of developments which can change the demand for electricity or the need for nuclear power.'

At present BNFL are chasing a West German contract for 4,000 tonnes of spent fuel. The Germans have decided to abandon the idea of reprocessing it themselves because of economic and environmental concerns.

Of course the industry ignores the fact that over the years the arguments used to justify and support reprocessing have crumbled. Marjorie recalls 'They said they couldn't stop the magnox plant because at that time they had to go on with the magnox because the fuel corrodes. Of course, they were unscientific about it. They could have stopped then. They said they had to go on. I knew the trouble they had with the fuel in the ponds, I didn't know that it could be put in dry stores, but Friends of the Earth did. They told the Windscale Inquiry in 1977. But BNFL had gone on putting the stuff in water and had gone on saying they had to reprocess it.'

That very simple statement points to one of the worst impacts of reprocessing, the flagrant pollution of the Irish Sea. It might seem that there has been so much written about Sellafield and its discharges that there is nothing left to say. Most people know that the Irish Sea is radioactively contaminated, yet few people can grasp that this is as a result of deliberate, daily discharges. Worse still, these discharges, which could have been avoided, were not only authorised by the government, but increased at different times to allow for the whims of the nuclear industry.

Successive governments have ignored the irrefutable evidence of even their own Committees. The 1986 report from the Environment Committee noted, 'all but one of the arguments adduced by BNFL in favour of an expanded reprocessing programme have little merit'. That one argument was that BNFL insisted that spent fuel, especially magnox, has to be reprocessed, otherwise it corrodes, but this is only because they keep it in water. The Commons Committee had recommended that the industry look at the cost of dry storage of magnox fuel, and drying out that which had already gone into water, and that this should be compared to the cost of reprocessing and waste disposal. The Committee's recommendations were not taken up. The Commons report noted that Sellafield was the 'largest recorded source of radioactive discharges in the world and, as a result, the Irish Sea is the most radioactive sea in the world. That the UK, with a relatively small nuclear industry, should be so dramatically out of step is a cause for concern.' In March 1989 letters that Walter Marshall, head of the CEGB, had written to Peter Walker (then Energy Minister) show that dry storage was a preferred option. In fact Marshall writes of how difficult he found it to argue against the environmentalists on this point. Had BNFL undertaken dry storage from the beginning, which was possible, then the whole contamination of the Irish Sea would have been avoided. This partly explains why the CEGB now wants to build a dry-store for all AGR fuel near the Heysham nuclear plants. Industry sources say BNFL's way of handling fuel is too costly in both financial and environmental terms.

The Environment Committee report also said that 'Sellafield is our primary interest here. Not only is it not glamorous, it has become a byword for the dirty end of the industry in the nuclear world.' Sellafield is dirty indeed, its two-kilometre pipeline stretching out into the Irish Sea spews out two million gallons of radioactively contaminated water every day. Over thirty different radioactive chemicals are poured into the sea on a routine basis. It is estimated that up to half a tonne of plutonium has been dumped in this fashion. One-millionth of a gramme of that substance, if inhaled, can cause lung cancer. The practice is archaic and typifies British environmental brutishness. But the other side of the coin is the fear that to have zero discharges would make reprocessing so expensive as to cause the plant to close.

Bill Maxwell hit back at the report. 'I do not believe the dry storage method is suitable as a long term alternative to reprocessing. If we are to have a nuclear industry in the long term then, for safety's sake, we must reprocess. Any dry store would need improved surveillance against the risk of fire and nuclear criticality. The radiation hazard would not go away and would be there for thousands of years.' Reprocessing does not decrease the amount of radioactivity there is. Whether we reprocess or not we will still have high-level nuclear waste to deal with. To give the reader an idea of scale the amount of radioactivity which had so contaminated the Irish Sea is only one ten-thousandth of that which is kept on site at Sellafield. Members of Maxwell's own union helped build the dry store which operates at Wylfa and would also work on the dry store the CEGB is presently trying to force on Heysham.

Experts in the field of dry storage saw things quite differently. David Deacon, of GEC energy systems, said, 'It can be demonstrated that it is significantly cheaper to store fuel for medium to long periods and then commit it directly to a geological repository rather than to commit fuels to the reprocessing cycle.' (n/s 3.3.83).

BNFL took another course altogether and opted to spend money on cleaning up the discharges, at huge cost to the taxpayer, rather than properly address the problem. For the last few years the company have claimed the sea discharges are going down, but they are still adding to an already contaminated environment. Of the whole nuclear fuel cycle, reprocessing is the most environmentally contaminating. Of the total radiation dose to the European community, from industrial sources of radioactivity, the largest dose is due to Sellafield's sea discharges. The nuclear reprocessing industry, which is not considered essential to nuclear power generation, faces a battle on all fronts to try to secure its future. In May 1989 the Conservative-controlled House of Commons Energy Committee issued a report in which they said BNFL was technically insolvent, because of the massive loans it had. In 1982 alone BNFL borrowed £50m from the European Investment Bank, and a further £60m in 1986 (w/n 17.1.85). From 1984–85 the company received grants of £31 million from the UK government, £25 million of which was regional development money, plus other grants and loans totalling £121m. The Energy Committee told the company that it could not afford to be complacent after the year 2000.

There can only be one justification left for reprocessing, apart from the jobs in West Cumbria, and that is for military reasons. It has been said that the children with leukaemia in West Cumbria are the early victims of the Third World War. BNFL admitted at the 1977 Windscale Inquiry that some two-thirds of the plutonium discharges were from 'other activities' on site. This polite euphemism was accepted as the British way of answering sensitive military questions.

6

There is a pleasure in the pathless woods,
There is a rapture on the lonely shore,
There is society, where none intrudes,
By the deep sea and music in its roar,
I love not man the less, but Nature more.
'Childe Harolde', Byron

In order to measure the level of pollution caused by man-made substances such as the Caesium-137 released from Chernobyl, the only bench mark of 'normality' we have to go by is the radio-activity spread across the globe from the atmospheric weapons testing of the 1950s and 1960s. Hence the expression that a certain place has 'above background' or 'above fallout' levels. Therefore the contamination resulting from the plutonium discharge from Sellafield can only be measured against existing radioactivity levels from fallout. The concern felt by people living along the Cumbrian coast is easy to understand from the map on page 100. As it shows, the levels of Plutonium-239 and Americium-241 (another toxic alpha emitter) are greatly increased here above normal 'fallout' levels.

Much of that contamination could have been avoided had BNFL been made to apply the best technology. But instead lax authoris-ation certificates gave the industry almost *carte blanche* and pro-vided no incentive for a sound environmental policy. For example, the permitted level for alpha emitters from Sellafield, licensed by Government departments, from the early 1950s, was originally 1,800 curies (a measure of radioactivity). In 1972, this was allowed to rise to 6,000 dropping to 378 in 1986. It is believed the massive increase in the early 1970s was to accommodate the increased levels that would result from oxide reprocessing. During this period the levels of radioactivity from the French plant of Cap de la Hague have only ever been allowed to reach ninety curies per annum.

BNFL argue that the reason their plant was technically so inferior to France's was because the French plant, even though it was dealing with the more radioactive oxide fuel, was newer. It was then revealed that the French have another reprocessing plant inland at Marcoule. This military plant had been designed and built prior to the present B205 reprocessing plant at Sellafield, but had, astoundingly, discharged only one ten-thousandth of the amount of alpha emitters BNLF had dumped.

In 1980 the dumping of solid 'low-level' waste at sea was still carried out by the UK. At that time Britain dumped some 95,000 curies per annum into the deep Atlantic trench some 400 miles off the Spanish coast. In twenty-five years of dumping the US had put 'only' 90,000 curies into their own western Atlantic dump site. In that same year Margaret Thatcher signed a Commonwealth protest against Japanese plans to dump nuclear waste in the Pacific. In the same year 200,000 curies of radioactivity had been dumped in a loose, liquid mobile form in the shallow waters of the Irish Sea.

The second line of defence taken by BNFL is that although other plants might be cleaner, what did it matter as long as people were safe? To test this theory they carried out a survey of those whose lifestyle or eating habits meant that they were far more exposed to radioactivity from the discharges than the average person. These were the 'critical group'. First tests centred on the people who gathered seaweed along the Cumbrian coast, next came fishermen who tended the salmon garth at Ravenglass. When this salmon run fell into disuse the scientists then turned to the fishermen at Whitehaven who came into direct contact with contaminated water, ate the contaminated fish and shellfish they caught and spent a lot of time in the contaminated harbours, like Maryport and Whitehaven.

Some fishermen have expressed concern over what was happening to the fish. Joe Stevenson is an onshore fisherman who worked out of Askam, a small village some eighteen miles south of Sellafield. It lies on the south of the Duddon Estuary, a shallow bay ideal for line fishing. Over the years Joe noted a marked decline in the number of flat fish. He was also concerned about the state of the fish he caught. Joe remembers, 'In spring you'd be catching young flounders. You would pick them up and the firm flesh would have the smallest of imprints on it. Recently we've

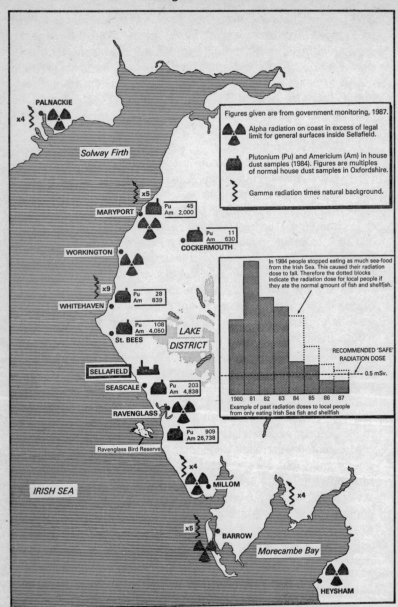

Figures given are from government monitoring, 1987.

Alpha radiation on coast in excess of legal limit for general surfaces inside Sellafield.

Plutonium (Pu) and Americium (Am) in house dust samples (1984). Figures are multiples of normal house dust samples in Oxfordshire.

Gamma radiation times natural background.

PALNACKIE

x4

Solway Firth

x5

MARYPORT
Pu 45
Am 2,000

Pu 11
Am 630
COCKERMOUTH

WORKINGTON

x9
Pu 28
Am 839
WHITEHAVEN

Pu 108
Am 4,050
St. BEES

LAKE DISTRICT

SELLAFIELD

SEASCALE
Pu 203
Am 4,838

RAVENGLASS

Pu 909
Am 26,738

Ravenglass Bird Reserve

x4
MILLOM

x4

IRISH SEA

x5
BARROW

Morecambe Bay

HEYSHAM

In 1984 people stopped eating as much sea-food from the Irish Sea. This caused their radiation dose to fall. Therefore the dotted blocks indicate the radiation dose for local people if they ate the normal amount of fish and shellfish.

RECOMMENDED 'SAFE' RADIATION DOSE

0.5 mSv.

1980 81 82 83 84 85 86 87

Example of past radiation doses to local people from only eating Irish Sea fish and shellfish.

Radioactivity Levels along the Cumbrian Coast

been picking them up and the flesh is soft, weak, as if it had already been cooked. I know that's not very scientific and I'm not suggesting the radiation is "hot" in that sense, but you get a feeling something is wrong with them.' Joe's fears have been echoed many times by local fishermen. Numerous fish have been brought to us with white cauliflower-type growths on their mouths, gill openings and skin. Flat fish have been brought in with the white underside tainted brown 'as if it had been toasted'.

Much of the early public concern surrounding Sellafield's sea discharges was based on anecdotal evidence such as strange markings on fish. After the Windscale Inquiry in 1977 the discharges did begin to come under closer scrutiny from the scientific fraternity. But until then very little notice was taken of what was going into the Irish Sea. A good example of this came in 1971 when BNFL wanted to increase the amount of alpha emitters discharged. These radionuclides, such as plutonium, are considered to be very dangerous. BNFL wanted the level raising from 1,800 curies per annum to 6,000. At the time the radiation advisor to Cumbria County Council, Professor Fremlin, wrote to Hugh Howells, the UKAEA manager on site. Fremlin asked if Howells thought BNFL's application to increase the levels was safe. Howell's reply was that not only did he think 6,000 curies was safe, but that up to 72,000 curies could be discharged each year without any harmful effects.

Although much debate now centres on the health of the alpha emitters it would be wrong to assume that no hazard is posed by the radionuclides which emit gamma or beta radiation.

Gamma emitters give off rays which are very penetrating, but many gamma emitters quickly decay in non-radioactive substances. Beta emitters, which send off particles which can penetrate into skin, are also less damaging than alpha emitters. They also tend to be much shorter 'lived' than alpha emitters such as Plutonium-239, which has a radioactive half-life of 24,000 years. Because of this difference in biological hazards of the different radiations emitted gross overestimates of 'safety limits' were initially put forward. After only two years' discharges into the Irish Sea, John Dunster published a paper in which he predicted that 100,000 curies of gamma/beta emitters could be discharged every month. This could have led to 1.2 million curies per annum going into the sea. In the end the highest that Sellafield was allowed was 300,000 curies of gamma and beta. It is those discharges that have cost millions of pounds of taxpayers' money to reduce.

The nuclear industry points out that the impact of radioactive discharges, to local populations, is limited in two ways, firstly by restricting the amount discharged, and secondly, by monitoring and assessing the actual radiation dose received by people. The body which recommends safe radiation exposure is called the International Commission of Radiological Protection. Over the years this has been heavily criticised by those who believe it is influenced too strongly by ex-civil and military nuclear scientists who sit on the Commission itself, or its various committees. For example, Dunster still sits on the ICRP, as do a number of ex-nuclear industry employees from various countries.

Nobody on the ICRP is an official government representative. The ICRP has no legal status in any country, yet its recommendations are accepted as the local maximum by most nations. However, open criticism of the ICRP and its setting of dose standards has come from some countries. America rejects the ICRP 'safe level' of 5 milli-Sieverts per annum for a member of the public by advising a level of 0.25 mSv. The German limit is 0.3 mSv. The UK legal limit of 5 milli-Sieverts for members of the public is equal to a hundred chest X-rays. The ICRP recommended levels for the unborn and children is the same as for adults. The reputation of the ICRP was called into question in 1987 when Professor Roger Berry, an ICRP member, left the National Radiological Protection Board to go and work for BNFL as their director of Health and Safety. Berry had been an active member of the Committee on the Medical Aspects of Radiation in the Environment (COMARE) the successor body to the Black Committee which looked into childhood leukaemias in Seascale. Although he resigned his place on COMARE as soon as he took up employment with BNFL, it was not until early 1989 that he stepped down from his place on the ICRP.

Not all the radionuclides discharged were actually controlled by the site-licence. Some, like Plutonium-241, were considered by the industry and government departments to be so harmless that they could be discharged in virtually unlimited quantities. Plutonium-241 has a half-life of only fourteen years, after which time it decays into the far more toxic and dangerous alpha emitter Americium-241. So much Plutonium-241 was discharged that even in seventy years' time more Americium-241 will be generated in the Irish Sea than was discharged directly from Sellafield at the height of the discharges in the mid-70s!

It was this sort of practice that led some people to express concern over the marine discharges well before the present outcry. Professor Vaughn Bowen is a leading expert in the field of oceanography and was a US delegate to the International Atomic Energy Authority. Bowen appeared in a Granada TV documentary in 1976 which showed that plutonium-bearing sediments from the sea could be blown onshore, dried out by the wind and get into people's homes. He said, 'I believe that the statement that present levels of radioactivity in the Irish Sea give no cause for concern is true only in the short term. Windscale has accumulated relatively close to it all of the alpha activity it has so far released. The population in the area is I believe under extreme hazard from the possible re-mobilisation of these accumulated releases. If I were a member of the British population, knowing what I know, I would be very concerned about the present situation. I believe that the present ICRP limits on body-burden for transuranics, like plutonium, should be reduced by at least a factor of ten, probably more. You would find that a considerable number of the British population are already exposed to more than they should be. By that I mean exposed to levels that could significantly increase their danger of experiencing public health effects in terms of life expectancy or specific malignant diseases.'

Bowen was not a lone voice. He was joined by Professor Karl Morgan, internationally recognised as the father of health physics, the safety regime used to oversee health at nuclear plants. Morgan's credentials meant that he was too important to be ignored. He reiterated Bowen's concerns when he said, 'I believe that the present permissible level (of plutonium dose limits in humans) should be lowered by a factor of one or two hundred.' Referring to the Windscale discharges he said, 'I am not sure if you had to make the decisions today that you would choose that as an acceptable waste-disposal procedure. I'm sure that it would not be acceptable in our country and if I were on a committee to approve it I would cast my vote against this.'

Bowen had been brought over to the Windscale Inquiry to speak on behalf of the Isle of Man. The ex-speaker of the House of Keys, Sir Charles Kerruish, was a particular thorn in BNFL's side. His worries over the Irish Sea levels of radioactivity sometimes made him unpopular with fishermen from the island who were no less scared of financial repercussions than their mainland counterparts. However this never lessened his fervour for highlighting the issues which worried him. During a TV debate he heartily embarrassed the panel speakers, who included Jack Cunningham and Sir Giles Shaw (then junior Energy Minister), when he said that if Sellafield's pipeline had extended into international waters it would have been closed under international law.

In August 1986 the Isle of Man Government called for the closure of the plant. Sir Charles Kerruish claimed that the Government had shown a callous disregard for the island over the plant's hazards. The Isle of Man has asked Eire to represent its interests on this matter in the European Courts. The Irish are considering legal action in the courts over Sellafield's transboundary pollution. As Peter Walker said after Chernobyl, 'the polluter must pay'.

One of the first signs which indicated that Sellafield might be causing some wider environmental damage was the decline in the numbers of sea-birds nesting near Ravenglass. Tony Warburton, a local naturalist, had built up quite a reputation as the 'bird man' of Cumbria. He was concerned that there might be a link between Sellafield and the decline of the black-headed gull colony on the Eskmeals bird reserve, of which he was the warden.

Over the years various theories had been put forward as to why the bird numbers were decreasing. The most popular belief is that foxes are killing the birds on their nests. Another is that there has been some drastic effect on the food that the gulls eat, thus causing what is known as a 'crash'. The fox theory is hardly believable on a colony that is known to be centuries old, with records dating back to ad 700. The gulls had faced this predator long before man really took an interest in the area. Foxes are also known to be territorial so numbers would not necessarily increase, in fact in an area notorious for fox hunting (John Peel was born only three miles from the reserve) it is not likely that they would proliferate in such numbers as to be able to wipe out a whole colony of birds.

Of course, there are also two-legged predators, humans, which destroy fragile environments wherever they go. But this particular reserve has been more protected than most in Britain as it was the first. Those who remember the colony at its height tell of thousands of birds tightly packed on the sand dunes. So vigorous was the gull population that thousands of eggs used to be taken to be sold as a delicacy in shops such as Harrods, and the bird numbers still did not decrease.

At the beginning of the century one writer described the beauty of the sand dunes and their residents when he wrote, 'Below us lay a natural amphitheatre of grey-green grass that looked as if it were starred with white flowers innumerable. We showed our heads and the flowers all took wing, and the air was filled again with sound and an intricate maze of innumerable wings'.

In 1970 the pairs of nesting gulls were estimated at 10,650, rising to 12,000 in 1975. By 1981 the numbers were down to 2,213, with no pairs at all by 1985. In the spring of that year the birds had landed on the edge of the sea for their pre-mating ritual. Normally they would have then settled on the sand-dunes for the breeding season, but instead they took flight, never to return.

In 1977 testing of gulls' eggs showed the presence of plutonium from Sellafield, but in 1987 a study showed that the levels were so low as to be undetectable. However, the very sand on which the birds laid and hatched their eggs for a number of years was contaminated to levels many times higher than background level. Oyster-catcher chicks reared by hand by Tony Warburton, from eggs taken off the dunes, showed genetic deformities in their capacity to respond to simple signals.

The number of oyster-catchers, ringed plover, shelduck and red-breasted mergansers nesting on the estuary have also declined. One of the more stupid suggestions came from a university team which said that to encourage the birds to return wooden birds should be placed on the sand-dunes. As someone remarked, perhaps they should try the same with humans on the beaches to get the tourists to come back.

Meanwhile the discharges from Sellafield were beginning to ruin this beautiful coastline for its human inhabitants too. In the early

1970s Christopher and Christine Merlin moved to Ravenglass. Christine recalls, 'We had spent many happy holidays, including our honeymoon, in the Lake District'. Chris had first fallen in love with the area he had been evacuated to, Saltcoats, near Ravenglass, during the war.

'As a child he had always wanted to live in Mountain Ash, a big Victorian house overlooking the estuary. Unbelievably it came up for sale in 1973 and we managed to buy it! We also bought the general store (also the post office) in the village. I ran the shop whilst Chris continued to manufacture engines at home. Running the village store we got to hear all the rumours about the plant. Some of the stories that we heard worried us both, especially those that came from people who actually worked at the plant. One or two of these workers were extremely close friends. We thought Sellafield was like any other nuclear plant. We simply weren't aware that there was also a reprocessing plant that discharged into the sea.

'During the 1977 Inquiry Chris and I were two of seventeen local people who agreed to have a whole body monitor done to see what level of radioactivity had been taken into our bodies as a result of eating locally caught fish. We were very interested in this test, as I was pregnant at the time.'

The Merlins admit that, like many other people, they simply put most of their worries to the back of their minds. Chris told me, 'We were not particularly concerned about the health effects of radiation. We had read that BNFL were saying the levels of radioactivity from the plant were so low as to be harmless. We also read that the Ravenglass estuary was one of the most contaminated areas on the west coast.

'An event that really made us think was the arrival of the NRPB with a small, portable air monitor in August, as part of the inquiry. They asked if they could put this in our garden for a thirty-day test. This attracted a great deal of national and local media interest with what we regarded at the time as extremist headlines, such as "G-Men come to Town" (referring to the Geiger counter men coming to the village). The air monitor in the garden was a practical check as to how much of the radioactivity discharged from Sellafield was returning to the shore line and becoming airborne.'

After the NRPB's visit the Merlins found their thoughts turning more and more to Sellafield, for their eldest son Sam was at the crawling stage at the time. If the NRPB were monitoring the garden for radioactivity then the inside of the house could also be contaminated, especially as the house became very dusty after storms.

Christine recounts her story in a slow fashion, hardly believing what they have been through. It is easy to see how the pressure on them to take some sort of action must have mounted year by year. 'Joe Thompson, one of the scientists who represented the Network for Nuclear Concern at the Inquiry, came to see us to talk about the house dust. House-dust contamination had been raised as an issue for concern at the Inquiry and the Royal Commission Report on the Environment in 1976. But the NRPB had not followed it up. Joe asked for a Hoover bag full of dust for him to get tested. The contents of this bag were, eventually, analysed in America. At the time that Joe had called for the Hoover bag Chris read our insurance documents. We saw it excluded any claims if the house was affected as a result of contamination by ionising radiation. This was alarming. Everything we owned was in the form of bricks and mortar in Ravenglass.'

The bombshell hit in 1978 when Christine answered the door of Mountain Ash to Udo Sonhoff, a physicist professor from Heidelberg University. 'He told us that he had come because of an article he had read in the *Whitehaven News* about the NRPB monitoring. I remember thinking at the time that it was the NRPB who had attracted the media attention to us. I remember how shocked Sonhoff was to find that I was using the Hoover. He pointed out that this was the last thing that I should be doing as the Hoover would only resuspend the smaller radioactive particles, which in turn, were the ideal size to be inhaled. Sonhoff was extremely knowledgeable on the subject and his concern for our welfare was very genuine. Sonhoff had with him a very sophisticated Geiger counter which could test for the presence of radioactivity in living tissue. As a practical demonstration he tested the cat which showed a high level of contamination in its rear end! Sonhoff thought this would be due to the large amount of locally caught fish that the cat ate. We soon stopped laughing when Sonhoff said he was surprised that the authorities had not evacuated the whole coastal strip in that area from Ravenglass to Newbiggin!'

To the average reader Sonhoff might sound like the archetypal crazy scientist, wandering across the land scaring the locals. But Sonhoff knew that during the 1977 Inquiry the Isle of Man's experts had discovered that sediments near the pipeline were twenty-six times more contaminated than the waters of Pacific Islands contaminated by US weapons tests. Those islands had been evacuated twenty-six years previously (e/m 14.6.77). Chris told me, 'Sonhoff's visit was the turning point in our attitude towards the dangers that we faced living in Ravenglass. To have such a person come from one of the most prestigious universities in Europe and make these statements would make most people very wary. Christine had just given birth to our second son, Ben. It was then we first started talking of leaving Ravenglass.'

The Merlins had read an article in the *Observer* which featured a neighbour of theirs. The piece looked into the whole issue of radioactive waste dumping in the Irish Sea. The neighbour had been interviewed because he carried out the salmon netting, a job with which Chris helped him. It was said that because of this job the neighbour was a member of the critical group from the discharges. The man in question subsequently moved to the south of England.

Chris remembers, 'I was not happy when I found that the Institute of Terrestrial Ecology were collecting corpses of birds to test for radioactivity content. In fact following a conversation with one of the bird reserve wardens the ITE sent one of their scientists, Pat Lowe, to "reassure" us. He'd come to calm our fears about the birds and said that the sludge that came in at high tide was the stuff to worry about, but then we shouldn't worry about it. Did he not realise what he was saying? It was a peculiar way to calm people's fears.'

The Merlins did not have much longer to wait to have their worst fears confirmed. In October 1981 Joe Thompson telephoned to say he had at last received the result of the house dust tests. He said that both he and Professor Radford were extremely concerned at the results of these tests and in particular he told us that high levels of plutonium had been found. Chris remembers Joe saying, 'I've got the results and it's not very good.'

One of the reasons for Joe Thompson's concern was that he had seen the results of the study done around the USA Rocky Flats reprocessing plant. Following a large accident there in 1957 plutonium contamination had been spread over quite a distance. A contour map was done of plutonium contamination levels and this was overlaid with cancer rates for the area. The higher the plutonium level the worse the cancer figures. In fact Colorado State Health Department had laid down a limit of 1 pico-curie, a measurement of radioactivity, per gramme of soil for contamination. Any higher and action had to be taken before it could be used to build houses on. The level of one pico-curie per gramme had already been criticised as being too much as it was twenty-five times the national average for fallout from weapons.

It was those pico-curies that got Joe Thompson involved in the first place. He told me, 'I got hold of a report from the Fisheries Research Laboratory. Obviously it was full of pico-curies, I didn't have a clue what they were, I didn't know a pico-curie from a garden rake. I then got hold of another report which was a critique by the Union of Concerned Scientists on the West Valley reprocessing plant in America. The first thing that stuck out from the West Valley report was that the New York County authorities had set up their own monitoring department and they had been niggling away for a few years to get the discharges down. Even if you didn't know what a pico-curie was you could see there were a lot more of them around Windscale than around West Valley. The very fact that the New York County people were upset about their number of pico-curies and nobody was doing sod all about the thousands of extra pico-curies flying around Windscale really got me going.'

Joe Thompson and Radford were worried because the radioactivity of the Merlins' house dust was ten times higher than the maximum limit set for the Rocky Flats area. This meant it was 2,500 more contaminated than garden soil levels in the USA. Later the Merlins were to learn that the levels of contamination in the house would simply not have been permitted to occur in other areas of the world. As Christine said, 'And here we were with two baby boys scrambling about in it. My heart sank.' Later an NRPB report gave levels which showed Mountain Ash was 17,000 times more contaminated with Americium-241 than an Oxford house. Other houses in Ravenglass and other seaside places along the

West Coast have been found to have levels of contamination 'above fallout'.

After Joe's phone call the Merlins made renewed efforts to move. 'We went to Kirkcudbright, in south-west Scotland, to look at a house. On the day we went there a local newspaper had a headline in which local fishermen were linking tumours in the local gannet population with Sellafield's discharges. We had thought that area was far enough away to be safe. We then decided to move inland from the coastal strip, but we wanted to stay in the county as it is so very beautiful.'

In 1983 a team from Yorkshire Television appeared at the Merlins' house. They were making a documentary on the contamination of the area and also the high rate of childhood cancers. Joe had given YTV a copy of the house-dust contamination report. The Merlins realised now that the whole problem was going to be given national publicity – a devastating prospect. Chris remembers, 'It was then we learnt about the experiment, I felt so bloody angry that such a thing could happen and that my boys were part of what was seen as no more than a laboratory test. At the time we might have been moved to go and see the NRPB for advice, in fact we did consider it, but then we discovered that Dunster was the director and we just dismissed it as a bad job.' (Dunster, head of the UKAEA's health physics when the discharges were increased in 1956, had told a conference that the 'discharges have been raised as part of a deliberate and organised scientific experiment.') It was because of Dunster's role in all of this that the Merlins believed it would not be possible to get an unbiased view from the NRPB view on the effects of the discharges.

Before CORE came on the scene the Merlins were very isolated and had to fathom things out for themselves. Nobody else was on hand to help them through the legal and scientific maze. Chris said it was not easy having to come to terms with such a technical issue. 'We read the *Encyclopaedia Britannica* and that has a lot on the effects of radiation. As soon as we started educating ourselves we realised that we were making the right move, as no level of plutonium is acceptable. When you're making decisions for children you have to be careful.

'We went to seek legal advice. The solicitor we spoke to told us, without hesitation, that we would have to tell any prospective buyers of the plutonium contamination. This was, he said, something which could be considered a "latent defect".

'In September 1983 we went to see Jack Cunningham, and showed him the analysis of the house dust. We told him we'd written to the BNFL legal department to say we were trying to sell a house which legally had a latent defect, and which we had to tell serious buyers about. Cunningham said it would be very difficult for us to prove that it came from Sellafield, which we now know isn't so. It's easy to prove. It was a stupid thing for him to say as he's a scientist. I told him I was tempted to put an advert in a national newspaper saying there's a house for sale near Sellafield, complete with plutonium. He said we'd be in serious legal trouble. He said there was more chance of the children getting knocked over by a bus than being hurt by the radioactivity levels in our house. When the issue became a political hot potato he suddenly started calling for zero discharges. What's the point in doing that if you believe the results are of no consequence? Cunningham did write to the Minister of Energy and got the stock reply.'

When the documentary came out the Merlins thought its impact would be limited. I did not meet them until after the programme was screened and my first impression was of two very worried and beleaguered people. With Christine working in the shop it was worse for her as she met many more people. She told me, 'It's almost impossible to know where to start to describe the after-effects of the programme. It's very painful to even think about some of the things. I know West Cumbria is very dependent on Sellafield and Ravenglass is orientated purely towards tourism, so we knew we were not going to be popular. The locks on the post office were glued up the very night the programme was screened. Normally polite, friendly customers became rude and offensive, money was thrown across the counter. We bore the brunt of accusations that the programme was ruining the village and the local area, all because we had taken part in the programme. I think what I felt most disgusted at was the villagers' reaction to our children, who obviously played no part in the decision to appear on the programme. People actually spat at them in the street. It happened to me. I could not believe it, here I was in England in 1983 and I was being treated like a Jewess in Nazi Germany. Were their jobs really worth their honour and dignity?'

Christopher remembers another instance of local hostility: 'One woman who used to be a monitor at the plant, and whose husband still works there, told her children not to play with Sam and Ben. This same foul woman also threatened a six-year-old girl in the village that if she played with our boys then she would not get lifts to school or invited to parties. From a grown woman with three children that sort of attitude is barbaric. It's another form of discrimination. It made me cynical and sickened by my fellow man. Added to all of this was the interest of the world's media.'

Financial problems were looming over the horizon too. 'Before the television programme we had had someone who was very interested in buying the house. He knew of the problems, but afterwards said he felt he had to withdraw his offer to buy as he could not afford to tie his money up in something he might not be able to sell in the future. In fact he was a solicitor and was in the same partnership that Rex Toft was in. He was happy to buy the house in terms of health effect, but was advised by his colleagues that he would be putting money into something which would not recoup the capital outlay.'

To 'counteract' the effects of the programme BNFL organised a series of 'talks' around the area. In these talks the Merlins were specifically mentioned and accused by BNFL reps of being the family that attracted the TV cameras to Ravenglass. A letter in which the Merlins were referred to was sent to the IBA following a Ravenglass Parish Council meeting: 'The programme so alarmed certain people who had purchased fresh fish from the trawlers each week so that they could enjoy fish regularly throughout the winter that they threw the contents of their deepfreeze away. Also many people who have retired to the village have been receiving calls from worried relatives, some of whom have exhorted them to leave the area that they had saved up to retire and enjoy.'

The letter went on, 'The area depends on tourism for a major part of its income and employment. It is as yet too early to say what effect this programme will have on the 1984 and 1985 tourist seasons, but local hotels have already had cancellations from people who had booked weekend breaks this autumn. A number of residents in the village are trawlermen, owning their own boats. Their fish, which was eagerly sought after on the shore as it was landed, is now considered by many to be contaminated. As a result there is a likelihood that they either will be put out of business or suffer financial hardship. Following many years of declining population there has recently been a welcome influx of younger people into a new housing development in the village. As with all young people they will need to move as they progress up their career ladders. Effectively this programme has blighted their properties as if a motorway were to be built over the site. Could you please advise this council to whom these people should address their claims for compensation for loss resulting from the transmission of this programme? Also, what action do you intend to take to prevent any of them going bankrupt as a result of this programme?'

In the nineteenth century the managers sent in to oversee the crofters in the Scottish highlands would often write begging letters to the lowland lairds when things went wrong. It was never their own inadequacies or inactions that were to blame for disasters, but always someone else. The Ravenglass residents acted in much the same way. They were not to blame, but circumstances, capricious to the last, might cast them onto the rocks at any time. In short the people of the area were not prepared to face up to the reality of Sellafield's thirty years of pollution.

The Merlins' worries grew, as Christine explained. 'We had the post office dust analysed and found that that was as contaminated as Mountain Ash. I had spent the best part of three pregnancies working in that shop. The first baby went full term, but he died only hours after he was born.

'The final months in the village were not helped by the 1983 beach contamination incident. We were already trying to keep the boys off the beach, but the accident just added to our problems. At the time we were trying to sell our house a battalion of BNFL monitors with Geiger counters were daily combing the beaches in front of it looking for radioactive debris from the slick. Lorries would arrive and remove what looked like very large amounts of radioactive material. The NRPB were announcing their house-dust study, a few years too late of course. Questions were being asked in Parliament on a daily basis. Hardly the atmosphere to encourage a sensible buyer. The period between the programme and our leaving the village was a living nightmare.'

There were other, more personal problems to be faced. Chris

explained how supposed 'friends' turned their backs on them. 'One of my best friends at the time was the photographer that BNFL normally use, Roger Savage. We did many things together. He came to see me to take some photos of the house for a newspaper. He had been told that BNFL were aware that he and I were friends and one of the people in PR had advised him to end that friendship. That was the last time I spoke to him. If he'd been half a man he'd have told BNFL what to do.

'The landlord of the Pennington Arms made a drink called Plutonium Cocktail. His son, aged thirty-three, now has cancer of the lymphatic system which started in his testes.'

The Merlins have also had to suffer much rumour about themselves and their motives for appearing on the programme. 'Some people who'd worked in the labs at Sellafield said we couldn't sell the house so we'd put the plutionium there! One man, who'd been a monitor for thirteen years, said the radiation had come in off the granite chippings on the drive. It's a physical impossibility to get fission products off granite chippings. We had to live with all this in a village which until then had been idyllic. We used to go to the Pennington Arms and get the food scraps for our ducks and geese. One day I went into the kitchen and a woman, who had done various sewing jobs for us remarked, "Here's the man who is stealing the bread from our mouths." Basically she meant I was endangering her husband's job as he worked at the plant. That was someone who I'd spoken to for nine years. She couldn't look me in the eye and say it, but made remarks to others to make me feel like a leper.'

Thankfully not everyone was hostile. Chris remembers, 'There was one scientist from the plant who made a point of coming into the shop when it was empty. One day he told us, "You've done right, you've got those buggers up the road jumping." Little things like that made all the difference.

'Also before Christmas people from the Ministry of Agriculture, Fisheries and Food had come to clear up some of the slick off the beach. They were using tweezers to pick up the more radioactive pieces from the turf right in front of the house. One of them asked to use the phone and he asked if "this was the house". I said it was and he told me he wouldn't live there for all the tea in China. And he was a qualified MAFF scientist who also told us he agreed with what we had done.'

The letter Ravenglass Parish Council had sent to the IBA attempted to smooth over health concerns in the area. 'In twenty-eight houses which back or face onto the esturial mud and are therefore most likely to receive contamination there are thirty-six people, of whom twenty-one are over sixty-five, with a combined age of 2190 years.' Once again blame was laid only at the Merlins' doorstep. The letter went on to vilify them. 'Alarmist statements were made by one married couple out of a village with an electoral roll of 229 and a population of approximately 250.'

Yet there were serious health problems in the area. Tony Warburton's daughter Anne was born in Ravenglass. She had problems when her periods first started. Medical examination revealed she had a double womb and for three years she had an almost permanent period. It is uncertain whether or not she will ever be able to carry a baby. She also has only one kidney. Most would consider such a problem to be very rare, but not in Ravenglass. Another girl in the village has exactly the same problem, one kidney and two wombs.

Chris remembers, 'Cancer became rather the regular thing to be suffering from. If you raised it in conversation people shied away from the subject, it was taboo. When Christine was having Sam in Newcastle Hospital there was a local Cumbrian woman in the terminal cancer ward whom we would go to visit to try and cheer her up. We told one of the nurses where we came from and totally unprompted she said two-thirds of their cancer cases came from our area. When you hear that you can hardly be accused of being alarmist, especially when you then find out you have plutonium in your Hoover dust.

'After that we became increasingly aware of the large number of people suffering cancers and strange illnesses in the area. In two adjoining houses in the village three people had had their legs amputated for "circulatory disorders". The cottage I lived in as a child during the war belonged to a man, Buster Jackson, who died of multiple myeloma in April. He was never off the beach, in fact he had the beachcombing rights to Drigg shore.

'The secretary of Ravenglass Parish Council, Colin Robinson, the man who'd signed the letter to the IBA, used to work at Whitehaven Hospital. He told us members of staff were putting together a map of all the local cancer cases and unusual illnesses. After a year the map was getting crowded and someone higher up stopped it.'

The list of people Chris remembers who were ill is long. 'I remember at one of those BNFL meetings in 1983 when somebody stood up and asked if there was no problem why did YTV come to Ravenglass. The BNFL rep said you can blame it on one alarmist family. The man who asked that question was Brian McElroy, the Seascale chemist. He died a year later of acute myeloid leukaemia.

'Over the years Christine and I became aware of a number of cancers and other illnesses in the village. Up until the new houses being built, there were our two children and six others born in the village in the twelve years we lived there. Subsequent to that there have been two Down's syndrome children, one died and one is alive. Out of a total number of twenty-five births two Down's syndrome is an incredibly high incidence. Both sets of parents were born and raised in the village. We became aware very early on of the people dying from cancers. Running the post office you got to hear all the news. During my time there I saw stomach, liver, breast and testes cancers as well as peculiar blood disorders. In Waberthwaite area there was a woman I knew who had a malignant growth in her mouth from which she died. In fact there was a set of three houses in that valley with two cancers apiece in each. When I lived in London I only knew one person who'd died of cancer and that was an aunt.'

The Merlins' court case against BNFL was heard in the High Court in October 1989. They were claiming £150,000 in lost money and aggravated damages. It had been a long haul for them, not without much pain. 'We thought the fuss would last only a couple of weeks, yet six years later the debate is still as furious as ever. Over those years more and more people have come round to support our case, which is the only positive point on the delay it has taken to get to court. There have been regrets, but in the long term I believe we did the right thing. We had loved living in Ravenglass. We had worked very hard to be able to live there and had greatly enjoyed our life in the small community in the early years. I have little doubt that we would have stayed there for the rest of our lives. It was literally the fulfilment of a childhood dream. No one would willingly or casually give up living in such a beautiful area. I felt we had to move for the sake of the boys and Christine felt the same way.'

Two of the dogs the Merlins owned whilst in Ravenglass died of cancer. They also had to destroy some of their geese which were born with severe deformities. It made the genetic implications more visible. The birds spent a lot of time on the Ravenglass estuary. Christine told me, 'The first worry seemed to be how will it affect my business, the tourism or my husband's job, if he worked at Sellafield. Some actually said they'd have preferred it if the leukaemia had never been found. I found that difficult to live with. I felt upset that people could have such low aspirations for life in this day and age.'

Mountain Ash was eventually sold to a Sellafield worker who lived in it for only six months. The Merlins had been told to expect a sale price of £60,000, but in the end the house went for only £35,000. In 1982 the Merlins had started to buy Grass Gars farm, with a view to moving from Ravenglass. The farm rests half-way up the side of Harter Fell in the Duddon Valley. With pine forests to the back and open fields to the front, giving magnificent views of the surrounding mountains, it is a stunningly lovely place. However, this second dream home was also to be tainted by the nuclear industry. Chris admits, 'I can't say how I felt when I heard about Chernobyl. It basically washed over me, it was just another thing on top of everything else. I found it hard to believe that one family could be affected twice by the nuclear industry. Our sheep were banned from sale. I was almost numbed by the time Chernobyl happened. I couldn't see any light at the end of the tunnel.'

In 1987 a third and terrible blow befell the Merlins. Chris found that he had a degenerative disease of the brain, similar to Alzheimer's disease. The doctors have not yet given Chris's illness a name. Needless to say it has brought even more strain and sadness to the family. He is only forty-eight, yet he could die within five years. The illness, thankfully, is not progressing as fast as at first feared. Chris believes that a positive mind and an active attitude helps keep the problem at bay. Could Sellafield be connected? Chris told me, 'The first time I was in hospital there was a doctor from Christies cancer hospital there and he realised the relevance of it and knew the house I had lived in. He got very interested and he did a lot of tests. His comment was "if this got in the news it would send the balloon up."'

There is no doubt that the general public believes the Merlins took the right action. Science is now catching up. In 1985 BNFL finally admitted that the alpha contamination levels on some West Cumbrian beaches were higher than would be allowed within certain of the radioactive working areas in Sellafield. For certain surfaces, skin and clothes, the maximum limit is 100 pico-curies per gramme. At Ravenglass, for example, the levels were 212 pico-curies. A BNFL spokesman confessed: 'It is no secret that levels on the silt are higher than those we operate for working areas. But our limits for working areas err on the side of caution and are merely a safety limit, not a danger limit. It's completely different working for eight hour shifts in an area and merely strolling over silt.' (w/n 15.2.85). Of course, this fails to recognise the safety implications for workers like fishermen and bird reserve wardens. Or children in the area who might spend a considerable amount of time on the beaches. If you are under eighteen and work in a nuclear plant you are not allowed inside the 'active area' at all.

In early 1989 Friends of the Earth published a monitoring report which showed areas some two to three miles inland up the Esk Valley were four or five times higher for alpha contamination than the NRPB 'investigation levels'. BNFL said members of the public were not at risk as they did not spend as much time on the sand marshes as a worker does in Sellafield. However, this is not strictly true. One farmer was so annoyed he contacted us. 'I'm sick of listening to the plant going on about their workers. What about me? I've farmed along that valley all my life. I've spent many hours on those beaches and I have animals on the salt marshes. It might not matter to BNFL and the unions that I don't wear their overalls or carry a union card, but it matters to me and my family.'

In 1988 Maryport, Whitehaven and Newbiggin recorded their highest ever levels of alpha contamination, regardless of discharge reductions. Sellafield discharges can be measured at considerable distances from the plant. In January 1985 researchers at the Government Institute of Marine Environmental Research in Plymouth revealed that they had found plutonium from Sellafield in the Tamar River which divides Cornwall and Devon, and empties into the sea at Plymouth. BNFL spokesman were quick to challenge the scientists on this. But Dr Eric Hamilton of the Institute said, 'There is no doubt whatsoever that the waste we are now finding in the south-west comes from Sellafield.' (w/n 3.1.85). As Hamilton explained, radioactive materials carry their own distinguishing marks which enable scientists to identify their source. This is not that each atom is marked, but that the isotope ratios can 'finger' the origin. That is how the aerial survey of Cumbria, after Chernobyl, was able to identify Sellafield's mark of pollution around Ravenglass. In November 1988 the Euro MP Stephen Hughes publicised a leaked report from the French military. The authorities had assigned scientists to look at the levels of contamination at Muroroa Atoll and report back. In defence of their own bad housekeeping the French cited the fact that the areas around Sellafield were more contaminated than around the Pacific test zone.

The Merlins are not the only ones who have fallen foul of the minority element that supports Sellafield come what may. One event that stands out in my mind was the eventual confrontation between BNFL and YTV in Seascale parish hall. At one point a lady named Mrs Runton got up to speak about why she was worried over Sellafield. Her son Geoffrey had died, aged twelve, of a Ewings sarcoma, a cancer so rare that only two other cases were reported in England that year. To the eternal shame and disgrace of West Cumbria that woman was booed and barracked by people in the audience.

A common myth about Sellafield is that the only ones who criticise the plant are 'off-comers' – non-locals. Yet there are many locals who have voiced criticism because they believe a little more restraint over the years might have made for a safer industry. Tyson Dawson farmed next to Sellafield for almost thirty years. A few years ago he moved to another farm only three miles from the plant. He told me, 'My family came from Drigg originally. In fact my father's first farm is where the dump is now, so you could say we've been affected right from the start. We've farmed up at Calder since from 1942. Sellafield had just become a munitions factory, it was a few years derelict and then it was taken over by the Atomic Energy Authority.

'We had no land involved until 1953 when they started to come across the river and build on land that we were farming. We owned right down to the Calder River. When the plant was expanding it was pretty frightening, going up to such heights and putting such vast amounts of foundations in, pouring hundreds of tons of concrete underground before they started to build above ground. We did wonder at the time what they would need all this reinforcement for. We didn't realise at the time what it would involve, but we learnt to our cost, particularly after the 1957 fire.

'Sellafield brought a lot of scientists into Seascale and I doubt very much if they understood the community. I knew them very well at one time. The factory was small then and you knew almost everyone. But the factory expanded, and this is the danger you see, at first they were very safety conscious, give them their due. Some of them didn't understand, but they did try to carry out the safety to the limit, but as they grew bigger more problems began to creep in.

Tyson has had a number of animals born with deformities. 'I can't get any official veterinary confirmation of this, it's only my opinion, but we had animals with cancer. Mostly animals that were drinking out of the river. Ten years afterwards BNFL did own up that the river was contaminated and they carted most of the river-bed away. Obviously they wouldn't go to that expense if it wasn't seriously contaminated. These animals had cancer of the throat and it only seemed to affect the young animals. Either the new-born ones or twelve months old. They were the ones that lived on the farm all winter outside and were produced on the farm. These are the ones that got this mysterious illness. No one could explain why this was so. The vet would say that these growths were cancerous and there was no doubt about that.'

I asked Tyson how he felt after Chernobyl. 'When that happened it made me more doubtful than ever. What can you do when it's world-wide? If we get rid of it here what's going to happen in France, in particular, or Russia? Would they do away with it, because it means we'll have to persuade them to. As to the contamination I have my doubts as to whether Sellafield would make the job worse actually, because they'd put contamination there already.' Tyson's pessimistic view is shared by a number of other people who believe that Chernobyl brought home to people the hopelessness of trying to fight pollution which recognises no boundaries.

Tyson told me, 'Although I live near Sellafield, since Chernobyl I've felt there is no point in going, not that I would wish to go away. I don't believe in moving away. I believe in dealing with the thing you've got and get rid of it and stay where you are. You're only leaving the problem for someone else if you move away.'

Tyson took quite a strong line on compensation for land. He outlined the dilemma of an area that prospers on the surface because of the influx of new people. 'I don't think there should be compensation to those whose land prices are affected, because there's no way you can deal with this fairly. Some people will get compensation when others are entitled to it. I don't see how it can be worked. It's a thing that's very difficult to prove if it's caused by contamination, because it's something you can't see. You see what's happened in this area, not with land in particular, but with house and property prices, it's increased in value tremendously because of Sellafield. There is a demand and this applies to farm houses being converted. So it would be very difficult to sort out who loses and who gains. In spite of all the things I've said against Sellafield it's helped the economy. Everyone gains when the local economy is good. Whether it is farming or whatever, they are bound to gain, so it's had a beneficial effect as well as an adverse effect.'

What Tyson said about farm houses is correct, but it is difficult to sell a farm as a going concern. A secret report we have seen by a local surveyors firm which recognises the effect of Sellafield stated, 'It has been a well-known fact that before the Chernobyl incident farms in the vicinity of Sellafield nuclear establishment commanded sale values, on the open market, of at least £500 an acre less than those achieved twenty miles away and beyond in mid and East Cumbria. In fact it was rarely, if ever, that a farm in that area was purchased by anyone outside the immediate district'. One of the biggest buyers of farms in West Cumbria has been BNFL itself, who then leases them out at peppercorn rents. After Chernobyl official confirmation was finally given to Sellafield's contamination of land when some farmers were told that up to 50 per cent of the caesium on their farms was "pre-Chernobyl fallout", not from nuclear weapons'.

After the spate of 1986 accidents some people did see the value of their property fall, but would not blame the plant. In 1986 the local County Landowners Association confirmed that publicity about Sellafield was causing a decrease in house prices. Calderbridge farmer Phillip Stanley complained, 'The value of my land had fallen to virtually zero because of all the publicity that has occurred.' The CLA's branch chairman, Sir Thomas Jackson, noted, 'We are suffering from a fall in land values at the moment, but that is entirely because of the excessive and irresponsible coverage given to the situation by the media.' (w/n 17.4.86). Sir Thomas's remarks appeared on 17th April, some fourteen days before Chernobyl was to give a taste of the real impact of nuclear power to Cumbrian farmers.

Tyson acknowledged that not everything in the garden was rosy with BNFL. 'It has affected the tourist trade as much as anything, people in hotels more than anyone else. It will have affected the West Coast, Seascale in particular will be one of the places. No one will come for their holidays like they used to. When I was young Seascale was only a village, and I mean a small village. I used to go in the sea when I was a child, but I wouldn't go in now. I'm sure they poured a lot of this contamination into the sea, they thought they were getting rid of it. It doesn't disappear, it might dilute, but it's still there.' Sadly, Tyson Dawson died in the spring of 1989.

Things have happened in Cumbria that would not have been allowed in other places. Two years ago there were strong protests in Wales when the Trawsfynydd plant was going to experiment with reactor shut down. Those tests were abandoned, but at the same time it came to light that BNFL had already held three similar exercises on the Calder Hall reactor without them being made public. Many believe the Calder reactors should be closed down – and quickly as they have no biological shield. Although they were built for only a twenty-five year life the industry has allowed them to go on for thirty years. Yet a report leaked to the press showed that they did not have the necessary earthquake supports that would be fitted into a reactor now. There have been three earthquakes in the last ten years in the bed of the Irish Sea.

If there were a major accident most people do not think the authorities could cope. In a poll undertaken by CORE on the anniversary of Chernobyl 85 per cent of the people questioned admitted that they did not think that those responsible would do the right thing or that they had a viable evacuation plan. Most of the people felt that no evacuation zone could be too big. At present the evacuation zone around Sellafield is two kilometres.

The number of houses that can be built in the village of Seascale is limited because of Sellafield. In 1976 the Council was told that the population should not increase above 2,750. A local planning official told the Council: 'The basis of this advice is that people living close to the reactors are slightly more at risk than the population at large, and the smaller the population the less problems of evacuation in the unlikely event of a major disaster.' (w/n June 1976).

In December 1988 a hoax call about a bomb in a sensitive area of Sellafield put the plant on full alert. The call came at eight in the morning when the main body of the workforce was heading in to the plant. Only the local newspapers carried the story. The pictures that came out spoke volumes. Miles of cars stretching away from the plant as they waited to get in through the gates. The same would happen in reverse were there an accident. The manager of Heysham 1 nuclear reactor summed it up beautifully when, immediately after Chernobyl, he admitted: 'We do have an emergency plan, it may be inadequate, but to say there is no plan at all is a gross untruth.'

CORE has argued that all public buildings near nuclear installations should have klaxon alarms attached to them so that in the event of an accident people would know to shelter. We were interested to learn that all the sub-stations on the south-west Cumbrian coast opposite the Heysham plant had small Geiger counters attached to them to test if radioactivity reached them when there was an accident (e/m 2.12.83). When they get high readings they supposedly set off alarms at the nuclear plant. Of course, the public would still be none the wiser. The CEGB said that these monitors were not just at Heysham, but 'all over the place'.

In May 1986 the Fire Brigades Union called for the closure of all nuclear power plants because they don't believe they can cope with an accident. Dave Matthews, the union's national health and safety officer, said, 'We do not know exactly where we would fit in or what our tasks would be if such a disaster (as Chernobyl) happened here. At some point we would be included, but as a fire service we are not responsible for such matters within the nuclear industry. We are as frightened and unsure as everybody else, and this is why we do not want the secrecy. Where radiation is concerned many of our men would be unsure of what they would be dealing with and that is unlike their present job. When one looks at Three Mile Island and now Chernobyl it becomes increasingly clear that nowhere in the world is safe from radioactive clouds. We must redouble our efforts to disband all nuclear power stations where they are.' (g. 15.5.86).

In 1985 BNFL held the usual emergency exercise at Sellafield with all the usual people in attendance – except for that vital ingredient, the press. Nevertheless they said that the exercise had included the 'employment of twenty experienced media simulators'.

CHAPTER

7

Suffer little children to come unto me.
Gospel According to Mark

On 1st November 1983 Yorkshire Television screened 'Windscale – the Nuclear Laundry', a documentary which publicised the high rates of leukaemias in the village of Seascale and surrounding area. Since that programme was screened the issue of nuclear power and its links with childhood leukaemias has hardly been out of the news. Such was the impact of the film that the government immediately commissioned what became known as the Black Report, named after the chairman Sir Douglas Black. He was to investigate and report on the incidence of cancer and leukaemia, in under twenty-five year olds, in the village of Seascale and the surrounding area (Millom Rural District).

Nine days after the programme appeared Greenpeace found a very radioactive slick off the end of the Sellafield pipeline. A week later the public was warned not to use the beaches because of the accident. Over the coming months the public were to be subjected to a barrage of confusing statements and statistics as the warnings over the radioactive slick became enmeshed in the debate on the daily discharges and the leukaemia cases.

The local people were very disturbed by the high rate of childhood cancer and leukaemias in the area. John Urquhart, a statistician from Newcastle University, had explained that the chances of a child getting a cancer in Seascale was one in sixty, as opposed to one in 600 nationally.

In March 1984 Barrie Walker, one of the local GPs in Seascale, was worried because another case of leukaemia had been diagnosed in the village since the Black Report had been commissioned. He told reporters, 'I have brought my children back to live here and exposed them to that problem and it worries me.' However, another local doctor, Ian McAndrew, said Sellafield

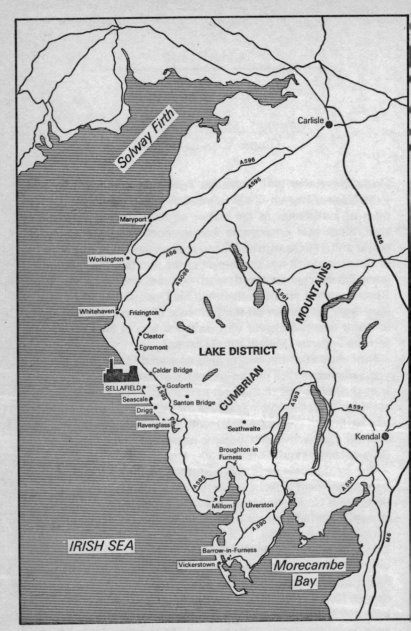

Cancer Incidence on the Cumbrian Coast

presented no hazard. He wrote in *World Medicine* that 'the relative risks of a walk on St Bees beach versus the benefits of the fresh air and exercise are greatly in favour of the walk.' At the time McAndrew wrote his article the 'beach ban' was still in force (w/n 24.5.84). Dr McAndrew later became a member of the BNFL medical staff.

Dr John Terrell, the District Medical Officer for West Cumbria, was particularly put out by the YTV programme because of course the investigation had gone on in his 'patch'. No one was blaming Terrell in particular for not noticing all the leukaemia cases. Nobody had previously looked at the figures for a thirty-year period and certainly not on such a local basis. The figures that are presented in most reports are on a health authority basis which are then put in with the whole county. Barrie Walker explained, 'It's hardly surprising that the Seascale incidence was missed, especially since it was over a thirty-year period and covered the careers of several different DMOs.'

However, Barrie did say that 'people had started expressing their fears about leukaemias before 1980 because they knew some of the workers had died of leukaemia.' But people had been assured there was nothing to worry about. 'I had talked to Geoff Schofield, who was senior medical officer for BNFL, and he said that they had looked at patterns of leukaemia around the plant and there was nothing at all to worry about. When I read the preview reports of the YTV programme in the *Sunday Times* it was quite alarming. One of my friends who was a senior manager in BNFL told me BNFL were desperately worried about the programme as they had seen a transcript. When I talked with my partners on the Monday, we came to realise actually there are a hell of a lot of cases. They had been spread over a long period and different doctors and at any one time nobody thought very much of it. We looked at the figures, then realised there was something that wasn't right. All you had had previously was large area studies and for Cumbria as a whole there was no problem.'

Before the Black Report got underway British Nuclear Fuels Ltd said that there was no increase in leukaemias in Seascale and the surrounding area. Barrie Walker told me, 'BNFL started trying to rubbish the fact that there was an excess. That annoyed me because we knew there was an excess and that is when I started to get involved. That they were trying to dismiss things that were true made me annoyed.'

The Black Report was published in July 1984. Black accepted the figures from the YTV programme which had shown childhood leukaemia rates in Seascale to be some ten times the national average. At that time, the investigators said that they could not establish a link between the leukaemia and cancers observed and the radiation doses resulting from Sellafield, as measurements of radiation showed doses were too low to be able to cause such an excess of the illnesses.

In response to the Black Report, BNFL claimed that the excess was a 'cluster' and that there were other clusters of leukaemias in places far away from nuclear installations. But the Black Report does not regard the high incidence of cancer in Seascale as a 'cluster'. A cluster is limited in time and geographical space; it can often not be explained and is regarded as a statistical aberration. However, in the case of Seascale the leukaemia rates were increased above normal for the period covering 1956–83. This suggests that some causal factor, such as radiation, could be at work in the area. The Black Report notes, 'Our initial concern was to establish whether or not there was an increased incidence or cluster of cancer, particularly in young people in the area around Sellafield. The word cluster, which has a technical meaning related to a concentration of cases in time and space, will not be used because we are concerned with an extended time period.' The nuclear industry has not yet found another area of the country with as high a leukaemia incidence as Seascale over such a prolonged period of time.

In January 1987 Dr Stan Openshaw released information which, he said, proved that there was a worse incidence of leukaemia at Gateshead, in the north-east of England (w/n 19.1.87). However, closer examination of the Gateshead figures shows it is not in the same league as Seascale. In Gateshead there were 165 cases for the period 1968–85, against an expected number of 100, a 65 per cent increase above the national average. In Seascale the rate is ten times the national average, 1000 per cent over the expected figure. The two areas are hardly comparable.

The Black Report considered a number of possible causes of childhood leukaemia. However, whilst not rejecting the possiblity that there may be other factors involved the report did contain the following statement: 'Radiation is the only established environmental cause of leukaemia in children within the limits of present knowledge.'

At the time the report was hailed as very reassuring, but in fact it was not so. The main thrust of the argument was that the nearness of Sellafield to Seascale as a factor in causing leukaemias was 'not one which can be categorically dismissed, nor on the other hand is it easy to prove.' The report found it impossible to establish the environmental levels of radiation around the plant twenty or thirty years ago. 'We shall never know the actual doses received by those children subsequently contracting leukaemia.' The possibility of undetected discharges having delivered significant doses of radiation to humans via unsuspected routes could not be entirely excluded. In February 1985 a UKAEA scientist, Dr Derek Jakeman, gave an estimate that aerial releases in the years 1954–56 had been forty times higher than those given to the Black Report. This radioactivity had come from the burst spent fuel cartridges in the Plutonium Piles that Piya Guneratne and Arthur Wilson had to push into the cooling ponds.

Barrie Walker told the press that he was astounded by Black's suggestion that family doctors in Seascale should reassure the public. 'Whilst he was in Cumbria, if he felt that strongly of our need to reassure the public, then he should come to meet me and my partners in order to express that view and try to convince us about that. I would feel that he is unlikely to be able to reassure me, or to encourage me to reassure the public. There is no way that I could reassure my patients in Seascale about the incidence of lymphoid malignancy.' (w/n 11.10.84). When Sir Douglas Black was asked if he would live near Sellafield he replied that he would consider it if there were 'no other possibility of a job elsewhere'.

John Terrell and Dr Martin Gardner (a statistician from Southampton University) were put in charge of collecting the basic information on leukaemias and cancers in Seascale. Gardner's interpretation of the figures given to the Black Report led him into a public row with James Cutler. Cutler pointed out that seven cases listed at the front of the Black Report were missing from the statistical interpretation given at the back. This lessened the impact of the leukaemia rate in Seascale and Millom and also the significance of the leukaemia rates in those places. Black had said that there was no obvious geographical pattern of childhood cancer in the Northern Region. Cutler, tenacious as ever, was not to be deterred. 'I obtained the detailed confidential evidence submitted to the inquiry by cancer specialist Dr Alan Craft of Newcastle and it shows that no fewer than four of the ten electoral wards in the region with the most significant childhood cancer rates are on the Cumbrian coast near tidal estuaries polluted by Windscale's discharges.' The top wards were Wampool near Maryport, Barrow Island, Seascale and Millom.

The view that all was well in Seascale was not shared by all the local residents. Understandably a number of people were very concerned with this issue and read the Black Report in depth. As a result CORE was approached with information concerning additional cases of cancer and leukaemia, besides those mentioned by Cutler. In 1988 Phil Reed, a volunteer for CORE, painstakingly went round the graveyards of West Cumbria and combed the death registers. His work bore fruit. CORE found ten cases which should have been included in the Black Report. These cases all conform to the age criterion time period which the report examined. In all, the Black Report dealt with some thirty-two cases of leukaemia, lymphoma and cancer. However, that document did include the caveat: 'It should be emphasised that the cases shown in the Tables may well be an incomplete list.'

The number of extra cases found by CORE totals 10–31 per cent of the total Black dealt with and a considerable number when dealing with small scale statistics. The cases omitted were: one non-Hodgkin's lymphoma, four cases of Hodgkin's disease, one leukaemia, two testes cancers, one bone sarcoma and one brain tumour. When we wrote to Black with the evidence he did reply and congratulate us on our work. However, it seems wrong that we, as a small group, should have spotted these cases when the authorities did not spot them.

I spoke to a woman whose child's death had not been included in the Black Report, even though it fitted in with all the criteria. Betty Crawford is a quiet woman, not the type to shout out about things. Life dealt her quite a blow when her only son died at the age of three with a brain tumour. Interviewing Mrs Crawford was not easy, it was obviously quite a strain on her. She now lives on the same council estate in Egremont as Joan King and Susan Clarke. For many years she and her family lived at the railway crossing at Saltcoats, near the contaminated Ravenglass estuary.

'I was born in Edinburgh. My family came to Cumbria because my father got a job as a construction worker at Sellafield. I've been in this part of Cumbria for about twenty-five years. My husband was born in Drigg, his family were either farmers, or foresters, that kind of work. His was a big family of six brothers and sisters. As the years went by I didn't really think about Sellafield or any dangers there might be. I don't believe people do think until something really happens to them and that's when you stop to consider it.

'My son took ill in 1983. We first noticed he was ill when he started being sick at the end of January. He had headaches and was sick when he got up. He was usually sick once then had headaches and was tired all day. He would just lie about and then he started to lose weight. This went on for a couple of months until, when the final month came, he had two fits just before they took him to Newcastle. To begin with I didn't know what it was. I didn't put it down to anything. The doctors diagnosed different things, throat infections, all sorts of different things.

'I thought the tiredness might be something to do with the fact that he'd just started playschool. In April I took him to the doctor's because he was sick again in the morning. I created a scene because the hospital doctor said he couldn't see him for six weeks. That night I got them to look at him. He'd begun to walk funny. Somehow I suspected it was leukaemia or a brain tumour. Since we had all arranged to go on holiday for two weeks the doctors said they would wait until we got back on 20th May. However, on 5th May he had a fit and died. I saw Dr Higgins in Newcastle Hospital that same night. He seemed to be the only one who knew what he was talking about. The next day, after he was dead, Steven was given a brain scan and there was the tumour. The doctor said it was one of the biggest cancers he'd seen in a child that age. In fact it probably would not have been operable on. The nurses told me that he was probably born with it. No one seems very concerned with how he got it. There was never any suggestion it was Sellafield.

'Not long after this came the Black Report about leukaemias in

Seascale. I did wonder if there was a connection. My husband, he never spoke a word about it. He's a very quiet man and doesn't talk a lot. Perhaps the biggest worry is that nobody does know. Nobody came to see us or anything. Dr Higgins was a great help, he was the only one who really did help us. Sellafield has got its good and its bad points. It brings a lot of work for everyone. I don't quite agree with all the dumping that goes on. The majority of people don't know what the results of all these things are going to be. A far greater effort should be made to find out, to make it safer. I think if it is ever proved that the discharges or anything like that has ever caused the death of one person then I think they should just cut them immediately because people can live without jobs. I used to wonder if in some way I was responsible for Steven's death, where it came from. Obviously you are just at a loss to think how it's happened to your children when it doesn't happen to next-door's child. My husband's family, they've all got children, about a dozen, and they're all perfectly healthy. Its hard to decide if there's any connection with living near Sellafield. I am very lucky to have two healthy daughters from a first marriage, they are now 27 and 21, in fact one is working at Sellafield.'

When I considered the implications of those ten missing children I was reminded of the metaphor used by the Canadian radiation expert Dr Rosalie Bertell. She sums up the official attitude towards health research in this way: 'If we regard the human beings alive today as our current account, and those to be born as our deposit account, it might be easier to understand. If we see people die and don't know why they disappear we should worry. If we estimate how many children we will have and they don't appear because of genetic problems, we should begin to ask questions. If a banker was to treat our money in the same flippant way that humans are treated we would soon protest.'

Rosalie also made the point that all the people who will ever live in the future are alive in our genes now. We have a clear duty to protect this heritage for the future. The exposure of pregnant women to radiation should be avoided whenever possible. In a letter to the local paper the former head of medical services at Sellafield, Dr Schofield, wrote, 'It has always been the policy of BNFL and its predecessors to ensure that any female worker who becomes pregnant should be removed from radiation work immediately. I must point out that such regulations have been in force from the earliest days of the nuclear energy project and are incorporated in the Sellafield site licence.' (w/n 12.4.84).

Dr Philip Day's analysis of sand from Seascale beach in 1983 showed levels of alpha emitters higher than would have been allowed inside the plant. Barrie Walker confirmed that, six years after the YTV programme, 'We still get people who are worried about getting pregnant here. If they were drinking local milk and tending to eat local produce I couldn't reassure them an awful lot. I just say you ought not to do that, stop doing that before you get pregnant which I think is sensible to be honest. I wouldn't eat local fish. I wouldn't drink local milk. I wouldn't go walking on the beach while you want to conceive or if you have just conceived because honestly we don't know yet if that has an effect.'

'Logically, I'd say, "Go away and don't have your child in Seascale." Forget about Sellafield, just think about the statistics. If you're going to have a child living in Seascale you've got more chance of your child having cancer. Logically, you'd say don't live in Seascale. That's a terrible thing to say.'

One of the more macabre recommendations in the Black Report was that people would be asked for still-born babies, placenta and miscarried foetuses to be given for plutonium testing. This was described by the District Medical Officer as 'biological material'. The Committee was trying to establish plutonium uptake, especially in foetuses, as it is thought that this is when radiation is at its most harmful.

The parents of the 'biological material' would not be told if plutonium was found. The Committee did not explain why they came to this decision, except to say that they thought it would distress parents. Had they considered that this might have avoided many hours of guilty self-doubt as to why a child had died?

That research was completed some two years ago, but has never been published. On New Year's Day 1989 a press release from West Cumbria Health Authority stated that the organs from the bodies of anyone under the age of 35 who dies in West Cumbria will also be requested for analysis.

It is established that plutonium finds its way into members of the Cumbrian public in levels higher than elsewhere. In 1986 a report published by the NRPB showed plutonium levels in West

Cumbrians to be from 50 per cent to 250 per cent higher than in people from other parts of Britain. Lungs and lymph nodes connected to them were found to be the most contaminated, but plutonium was also found in the ribs, vertebrae, femurs and livers. The bodies of younger people showed less plutonium contamination than older people.

There is also evidence to suggest that the rate of certain cancers, in both children and adults in the village of Seascale and its surrounding area, is worse than the national average.

The most recent for the patients who use the Health Clinic in Seascale show that there were three brain tumours from the years 1980–1989 against an expected number of 0.8. It is believed the figures are an underestimate because not everyone in Seascale is attended by the doctors at the health clinic. The figures are based on a population in the village of 2,000 people. The following are the numbers for other types of cancer which actually happened, with the expected numbers in brackets. Cancer of the larynx 2 (0.8), ovary 4 (2.8) and bladder 7 (2).

For the whole medical practise based in Seascale, which covers some 6,500 people living in villages mainly to the south of the plant, some of the cancer rates are quite alarming. Four cases of testes cancer have arisen, against an expected 1.56 for the years 1980–89. There were nine brain tumours in the same area, but only 2.6 were expected, giving a rate of almost four times the national average.

One of the most important recommendations the Black Report made was the establishment of an ongoing committee to look at radiation from various sources. This organisation is known as the Committee on the Medical Aspects of Radiation in the Environment.

In July 1988 COMARE published its report on the high incidence of leukaemia around the Dounreay reprocessing plant. Because of the earlier work on the Sellafield area COMARE concluded, 'However, the evidence of a raised incidence of leukaemia near Dounreay, taken in conjuction with that relating to the area around Sellafield, tends to support the hypothesis that some feature of the nuclear plants that we have examined leads to an increased risk of leukaemia in young people living in the vicinity of those plants.' Martyn Day, the solicitor who has dealt with most of CORE's cases, took advice from leading Counsel when he read the report. He asked us what would be the best way to get in touch with local Sellafield people with leukaemia and cancer cases who might wish to claim damages. Although we knew a number of people (we had already been approached by some to get cases started) we could not give him names and addresses. We told him the only way he could get in touch with people was to advertise.

The response was amazing, with some thirty-five families coming forward. A number of criteria were applied to choose which would be the best cases to go forward to court: the closeness of the family home to the plant; whether either of the parents worked there (work is now underway to look at the possible link between paternal exposure – especially to things like plutonium – and childhood cancers); where they lived when the child was born; the age of the child when it was diagnosed; the type of cancer they have; how far they live from the sea; how much use they make of the beach or how much they ate locally caught fish and shellfish.

Four cases were chosen to be the test cases. Dorothy Reay died in 1962 aged ten months of a lymphatic leukaemia. Her family lives in Whitehaven, very close to the coast. She died within four days of the first blood tests being taken. Her father was a Sellafield worker who died of cancer in 1977.

Gemma D'Arcy is suffering from chronic myeloid leukaemia, which was diagnosed in 1987 when she was three. Her family live at Cleator Moor and her father works for one of the contracting firms for Sellafield. At present her family are desperately trying to find a bone marrow donor to match Gemma's as this is her only hope of survival. Gemma used to go to play on the beach as a toddler.

The third case is Ian Renwick, who died of acute lymphatic leukaemia in 1971 at the age of three. He was first diagnosed at the age of twenty months. Ian's family live in Moor Row, a small village six miles north of Sellafield. His father worked on a farm at St Bees and died of a 'blood clot' in 1978. The family regularly ate local winkles and mussels which they gathered from the sea shore as well as eating locally caught fish two or three times a week. The family holidays would be spent on the Cumbrian coast.

The final case of the four is Vivian Hope, who has

non-Hodgkin's lymphoma. Vivian's illness was diagnosed in June 1988 when she was 23. She worked for a short time in the laboratories on site and later for a contracting firm at Sellafield. Her illness first started as a pain in her shoulder followed by a tingling sensation in her legs. By the time she contacted the doctor she was virtually paralysed and had to have an emergency operation to remove a tumour from her spine. She had to suffer three months of chemotherapy, resulting in the loss of her hair. Painful physiotherapy and a lot of courage now means that she can walk again with the aid of sticks. Her father had worked at Sellafield from 1956 until his retirement in 1988. He was a maintenance fitter and later a foreman for quality assurance dealing with plutonium pellets.

Vivian Hope's case is one of the six new cases of cancers reported, after 1983, in the area the Black Report looked at. There seems to be an increasing trend in all types of lymphomas, now nearly as numerous as leukaemias. In a village the size of Seascale the expected rate for lymphomas, for all ages, would be one every fifteen years. There have now been seven cases reported since 1980, giving a rate of nearly twelve times the national average. It is estimated it will be two to three years before the cases get to court.

When the leukaemia victims' families announced their intention to sue, a BNFL spokesman said he believed that if the Sellafield operations were found to cause the deaths of members of the public then the plant would probably have to close. This statement masks a very real dilemma to those taking cases forward. In such an emotionally vulnerable position these people do not need to feel that in addition to taking on such a big company they are endangering their neighbours' livelihoods as well.

Why do people continue to live there if it is so dangerous? The answer is that not all the parents of children with leukaemia accept that Sellafield is to blame. Terry White is typical of those who have to balance no job with what he sees as only a possible link with his child's ill health. His son William has leukaemia and is now in remission. Terry said he would uproot his family if he thought there was a connection. 'It would be a terrible blow if Sellafield closed, practically everybody here works at the plant.' White must have summed up many others' thoughts when he said, 'I'm certainly not frightened of working at Sellafield. I'm more frightened of not working there.' (*Sunday Mirror* 23.2.86).

It would be wrong to suggest that people like White stay because they only consider the jobs argument. After all, over the years a number of people have said that Sellafield is a safe place to live near or work in. Following the YTV programme, Professor Fremlin, Cumbria County Council's radiation advisor from 1971 to 1986, told the County Council, 'Quantitive analysis of the figures given in the television film shows that the hazards are trivial compared with the smoking of a single cigarette. The film and the activities of those who took part are doing major harm by diverting attention from a search for the real causes of the excess cancers observed, which could be chemicals, virus infection or X-rays during gestation but could not be due to radioactive materials from Sellafield.'

Over the years Fremlin has made some extraordinary statements in support of the nuclear industry. A founder member of CND, he passionately believes in the 'peaceful atom'. In 1984 he put some of his beliefs in a document for the National Nuclear Corporation. He said that because people contain Potassium-40, a naturally occurring radionuclide, 'Sleeping together in the same bed is a good way of getting regular doses of low-level radiation. This reduces the risk of cancer. Tests have shown that exposure to low, but regular radiation levels has led to prolonged life.' (d/m 6.3.84). At that time Professor Fremlin was still the advisor to Cumbria County Council on radiation matters relating to the world's most polluting nuclear facility.

Not everybody belongs to one camp or the other. In fact I have always been surprised at the variety of views which exist on the plant. Barrie Walker is a typical example. 'I have no feelings about the nuclear power industry one way or the other. The concept of a nuclear reactor itself doesn't desperately worry me. What worries me now is discharging stuff into the environment that's going to last there for a long time. They don't know what it does, because we don't know what it does radiologically or chemically for that matter. I'm certainly concerned about reprocessing. I think what was allowed to happen in the '50s and '60s and '70s by the government was criminal.

'The fact that lymphomas haven't stopped makes the villagers think about it. Most people accept that there is possibly a risk associated with Sellafield. At the moment they are balancing that risk with "you're better in work" and there is a risk wherever you live. If you think about it though, this area was once without risk prior to 1947 when there wasn't a Sellafield. The health of this area should be the same as any other rural area, which should be very good indeed.'

At one time Seascale was a thriving holiday village. The railway station, which now has one flimsy shelter, once had three newsstands, eighteen porters and thousands of people crowding onto the beach. *The New Illustrated Handy Guide to Seascale and District*, published in 1910, emphasises the healthy aspect of the small Cumbrian town. 'Diseases most benefitted by its climatic advantages are asthma and other respiratory diseases; nervous exhaustion supplies a rapidly increasing number of visitors; the brain fagged townsman finds Seascale a complete change and rest which he requires. Probably no other class of cases yield such good results by the air and water as the anaemia and debilitated from general loss of tone.'

The Medical Officer of Health in his annual report for 1908 states that the death-rate is 15.2 and the zymotic (disease) death-rate .01 per 1,000 for the whole district. Visitors to Seascale find that the invigorating seas and mountain air – 'pure, dry and bracing' – and outdoor exercise combine to induce natural sleep, and therefore Seascale has a high reputation for the cure of insomnia.

Barrie Walker takes a pragmatic view of things: 'What would I say to someone living in the village, who has got over their cancer or lymphoma, who says, "I've got this, should I go now?" I'd probably say no, to be quite honest. If you believed what's caused it it would be pointless, really, moving.' For various reasons the risks from the nuclear industry are perceived to be greater than other things.

'There is the potential for cancer which is very emotive. Seeing a child with leukaemia is a desperately emotive thing. They've obviously seen kids in the village die. Luckily I haven't seen kids die in this village because they are surviving now because of improvements in treatment.

'We don't know what the long-term effects on our genetics is going to be. They actually measure radiation exposure by chromosome damage. That's the big bits of radiation exposure. What do the little bits do? How many genes are getting affected there?'

Barrie was born and lived one mile from Sellafield. 'We owned a farm and in '57 my father had to pour milk away. My father then went to work there when we left the farm and my brother worked there later for a while as a health physics monitor. We came back here in 1979, because I wanted to work in the area I was brought up in.

'The contamination has completely spoilt my enjoyment of living in the area. To bring children up in the countryside, safe and clean, was our reason for coming back. Prior to 1983, in the summer the children spent the afternoons after school on the beach, where I'd spent many happy hours as a child. Mothers would take their kids from school at three o'clock down onto the beaches. I'd get home from work at half past five, everybody would be getting back covered in sand. After that, after '83, nobody's done that. We certainly don't use the beaches like we planned to use them or did use them before. That's actually taken away half of the pleasure of living here. There is always going to be a worry about the kids, especially the one that was born here.'

But Barrie is not alone in his fears. 'I see people who bring their kids here, when they get illnesses they visualise it is the early symptoms of leukaemias or lymphomas. They are more worried and understandably so, they become neurotic.

'I feel sad about what it's done to the area, desperately so. If there was an alternative, if people were honest with themselves, most people would say we'd have been better off without it. If people were offered jobs in other types of employment, it's speculation, but I think the answer would be yes. Still, for the workers there is a hell of a good pay packet at the end of the day. It is eight-hour shifts and it is very comfortable working conditions. You have to remember the vast majority of workers do not work in a contaminated area. Amongst those who work in the dirty areas, there is a great deal of concern there, but they work there more because they reckon they are earning more money. The possibility of accidents worries them. I listen to people talking about '57. It must prey on their minds a bit. They think about what happened at Chernobyl. They also have a fear of cancers, but a major accident is the main one. Some of them, when they get a bit older, they start to worry a bit. They think they might be making mistakes. I have come across this. If they get a measurement wrong they might have influenced how a process would go, or how much they were to discharge into the environment or whatever. You see that among the older guys as they get towards retirement age.

'The problem is that the industry demands perfection of human beings. A great problem was the NII report in 1986 caused a great deal of work. They couldn't actually cope with the recommendations without a lot of people working overtime. As we saw in '83 when somebody made a mistake, the potential was there, I think for one of them getting individually sued or put in prison or whatever for breaking the law. Never mind the fact that they might actually do harm to people.

'One way or the other Sellafield has stigmatised West Cumbria. The classic joke in alternative comedy seems to be about Sellafield these days, you'll glow in the dark mate, you can wave three hands or whatever.

'Sometimes people come to me when they are worried about radiation and I may have to reassure them. I've been put in very terrible positions about this on numerous occasions. I employ people in that I'm the course organizer for the training schemes and I've got twenty junior doctors around on this course and I bring them into the area. Very often I'm reassuring people who come into the area that it's quite safe for them to come and live here. It puts me in a very ironic position.

'There's still a quality of life to enjoy here that's not enjoyable in other places and I'm hoping it will go on for another hundred years for my children's children and everybody else. I'd hate Sellafield to destroy that. I think that's why I keep going. I think it's important that. That place probably won't be here in a hundred years, it certainly won't be active. It'll probably be a graveyard for the nuclear industry, but the rest of Cumbria will still be going. You want to maintain Cumbria because we won't have any other industry as far as we can see. We want to make Cumbria as attractive as possible and a good place to live in for the future.

'I know the people who built the plant, I know the scientists. I trust them as I know they are good people, but at the same time they are fallible and the decisions they are making must create a lot of quandries. I know them warts and all. I know people who are working at very high levels in the plant and obviously make decisions at various stages and they are all very fallible humans. I don't know anybody who is perfect who works at that plant. I'm not perfect, I make mistakes, you make mistakes. They are just like you and me. That's desperately worrying. I've seen them making decisions in other aspects of life which have been wrong. The other thing is the way the nuclear industry is propagandised. It's propagandised its workers into believing the radiation is safe. They've even got an article saying radiation is good for you! When you go on saying that people are going to believe you and do stupid things and that is also terrifying.'

CHAPTER

8

Do not go gentle into that good night,
Old age should burn and rave at close of day;
Rage, rage against the dying of the light.
'Do not go gentle', Dylan Thomas

Barrie Walker's views are based on many years' experience as a doctor, caring for the afflictions of the body. Peter Levitt, as Seascale's Methodist minister from 1982 to 1989, was there to help the soul along. He too has a degree, but his is in physics. It is interesting to consider the different attitudes engendered by the scientific disciplines of Walker and Levitt. For Levitt has faith not only in the future of the nuclear industry, but in the safety of it too. Thirty-five years old, Levitt was born in one of the coal mining areas of Yorkshire. His father was an engineer and his grandfather a coal miner. His earliest interests were in science. After gaining his degree at Durham University he went on to work in laboratories at Cambridge. 'I decided to be a Methodist minister then and did three years' training and was sent to Seascale, partly because of my scientific background.

'Having been brought up in a coal mining area and having seen some of the effects of that on the landscape and to some extent on people, although those I knew who worked in the industry were living to old age, I felt there was a place for nuclear power for electricity generation, that it was a risky technology, but that it was known to be. I remember from my school days learning about Marie Curie and radioactivity and the really rather harsh way in which the early pioneers were harmed by it physically.

'Admittedly there's the worry of concentrated radioactivity in a reactor or reprocessing of spent fuel and how they handle the waste. There may not be a lot of it but it is a difficult thing to handle.

'Most of my parishioners are Sellafield workers and people who come from outside the area who were not born and bred around here. Their children could be classed as Cumbrians, but the parents can't.

'You can detect very small amounts of radioactivity. What's handled is man-made, it's something which a fair amount is known about. There's always been the move to reduce the discharges, not wanting to harm the local population, because as time went on little amounts were accumulating. In common with the chemical industry it has had to find new ways of dealing with waste.

'I think there's also internal pressure. From my limited experience as a scientist, you're not happy with the old practices, things are quickly out of date. Scientists and technologists are always interested in improving and changing things.

'It was the media attention that's been more of a problem rather than what's actually happened at Sellafield. My physics degree has come in handy when asking people questions to improve communications. Some fairly senior workers were aware of what was going on and were able to pass on some things. I have tried some sort of perspective so that what happens at Sellafield cannot be sort of "explained away" or excused, but set in the context of what happens in other industries. In the coal industry what was acceptable in terms of slag heaps back in the early '60s is not acceptable now.

'I would rather there was no need for any weapons; nuclear, biological, chemical or conventional, but sadly there is seen to be a need for them. Although I am not happy with the idea of nuclear weapons I have not felt it would be useful to make any great issue over opposing them and opposing Sellafield because I feel developments at Sellafield have moved much more to the civil use rather than the military. The electricity generation, the experimental work on the Fast Breeder Reactor, that has been a worthwhile and acceptable human endeavour. I could support that. I look forward to the day when we can do without nuclear weapons, but when that comes I think there'll still be a place for nuclear energy to some extent. It was recognised there was a need to improve communications. There'd been a very secretive military background to what goes on at the site. That's still there but that was the dominant thing at one time.

'I've had contact with older people who've had cancers and none of them or any members of their families have blamed Sellafield for their ill health. I haven't had any contact with children or older ones where there's been any expression of Sellafield being to blame. I had to face the question when I came here in 1982. Our older boy was born here three months after we came. When we thought about having another child, after the YTV programme, I did think it would be right to do this. I looked at the evidence as far as I could, I talked to people and then decided, yes, it would be OK to have another child. The boys are now four and six. Some of the older people I've known who've had cancer smoked as well as working at Sellafield. Again it's a matter of balancing risks. I'm happy to let my children on the beach. We have played on the beach. I did at one time have an air monitor in the house. I haven't seen a copy of the full report, but it appears nothing showed up compared to figures published by the NRPB or sampling done by any other group.

'There was unease and upset caused by the YTV programme, but the Black Report presented a more positive picture than presented by TV and media. People have felt they were happy to stay on, there's no evidence of people going.

'I visited the site within a couple of weeks of coming here and then again a couple of weeks ago. There have been some big developments. Some of the people who've criticised Sellafield have limited their thinking to what was going on until the late '40s or '50s, up until the '57 fire – perhaps a little of the reprocessing into the mid-60s – and have failed to appreciate continuity of development in terms of reducing discharges. I haven't been too impressed with CORE, the local group. They've picked up on discharges and leaks. It's been rather a gut reaction to what's going on.' The Reverend Levitt is quite right to criticise those who do not at least go to listen to what Sellafield has to say. However, after our five site visits and numerous debates I do not think such a charge can be levelled at CORE. What is perhaps interesting is that in seven years of living in Seascale the Reverend Levitt never once contacted CORE nor, to my knowledge, did he attend any of the meetings we arranged.

Of course, both the Reverend Levitt and Barrie Walker are lucky not to have children who have been affected in any way. It's not so easy to be calm when your child is ill and you think it might be caused by the plant. Janine Allis-Smith explains: 'I grew up in Holland. I first came to Cumbria in 1961, I was twenty-one. I came to the Lake District because it is very beautiful. I was thirty when I was expecting Lee. We had moved to the Broughton area and were very pleased to be able to buy this farm house, because it was near the coast.

'I thought life could not be more idyllic. I came from a big city, never really lived in the country. To exchange a flat country like Holland for mountains, fields and the sea was quite amazing. I reckoned I was very lucky. We found Lee was ill when he was twelve. He was very much into fell-running, trained quite a lot and did a lot of racing. After reaching his peak and winning everything he suddenly wasn't fit any more.

'It was August 1983 when the signs of something being dreadfully wrong were so obvious, because he had bruising all over his body. He had been to a fun park where they had been on little bumper carts. He had bruises, massive bands around his wrists, he really looked as if he'd been run over by a lorry. I immediately took him to the doctor and when he made Lee take his clothes off to have a look at him I was horrified, the bruising was everywhere. The doctor at first tried to tell me that it could be a virus, but I didn't believe him. I saw the look on his face, the panic when he took a blood test. I knew there was something seriously wrong. That night when I got home and I saw him in bed, I knew he was dying at that time. I knew it. I just looked at him and thought this is something so dreadfully serious that he is dying.

'The next day the doctor phoned and said they wanted to take further tests. He didn't say that it was leukaemia, but I knew. It's difficult to say what I felt. It was like a nightmare, I couldn't take it in. I think I ran out. I screamed my head off because I couldn't believe it. This horrible shock. All I could see was that he was going to die. Something you don't expect at all when you have all these dreams about your kids. I think the thing that keeps you going is seeing them in the future and what they are going to do and seeing them grown up. Burying them is not really featured in that. It was more difficult because I could not frighten Lee. I had to behave normally. Not let him see I had been crying. The hospital blood tests confirmed that it was an acute lymphoblastic leukaemia with a T-cell complication with it, which did lower his

145

chances. They gave him about 40 to 50 per cent chance of surviving.

'It was very comforting to get to Manchester because they weren't dispirited. There was no drama in it. Their casualness gave us confidence. There was a whole ward full of them. It was strange, you were hungry for information. You go around desperate to know what is the matter with other kids, what stage are they at, how long have they been diagnosed and how long they have kept alive. You know, what are their chances. To see a child that's alive a year after his diagnosis and looking quite well was the best hope really.

'The second after I was told there was hope I had hope. I found a sort of determination that whatever was to be done, if there was any chance, Lee was going to have it. That sort of overcame the grief and desperateness of the whole situation. Tony, my ex-husband, was different, he couldn't face it at all.

'After the initial shock of learning that Lee had got leukaemia, then the hospital treatment, then you start asking "Why?" Lee was diagnosed in 1984, which was after the first report came out about the connection with radiation and Sellafield and childhood leukaemias. It was strange because having been to the ward and seeing the treatment the kids go through, the masses of injections which are really quite horrendous, the sickness – when I saw all this controversy about Sellafield, I just couldn't believe it, when I saw what those kids went through, that a place that was on our coast could be responsible for that.

'I thought that if anybody knew this was happening and possibly caused by the industry they would not allow it, they wouldn't want to operate it. I couldn't believe that it was Sellafield. I thought that there would be a keen interest in clearing the name of Sellafield and finding out why the leukaemias happened. I thought the best person to contact was the medical officer Dr Terrell. When I phoned him up I got the biggest shock of my life. He didn't want to answer my questions and when I said in fact that although we lived most of the time in Broughton, which is just half a mile across from the boundary of Copeland, that we had a house in Copeland that we paid rates on, and could Lee be included on their list of leukaemias, he said that as Lee's main address was in the Duddon he couldn't possibly be included on a list for Copeland. He said he knew somebody, a doctor who was interested in leukaemias and would pass the name on. I had seen your name in the paper and that you were taking up the cases and I thought I would see whether you could give me some more information.

'Some articles by Dr Alice Stewart, about her research into the connections between the increase in the rate of childhood leukaemias after their mothers had been X–rayed, made me think about how that fitted our lifestyle. When the discharges were high in the 1960s and 1970s we spent a lot of time of the beach, particularly the summer when Lee was conceived, to me it was a particularly good summer. When Lee was born we had a camper and so we used to travel up and down the coast. We used to go to Drigg, because it was a nice beach and you practically had the beach to yourself. We used to play in the streams that come from the dump, we used to put Lee in pools to play.

'When I read about radiation I felt guilty because I had taken Lee to the coast. I can't look at the water and not feel it's dangerous. When I see children in it I sort of cringe because of the possible dangers to them. I would like to go and see their parents and say "do you know what could possibly happen?" I can't understand people who still take their kids on the beaches. I think they must be mad. Sometimes I feel they are using their children to prove to themselves that it's all right, which is absolutely ridiculous. I mean, there are some people who believe that smoking isn't bad, but you wouldn't give a child a cigarette, would you?

'I feel angry with the PR people from the nuclear industry. They talk down to you, try to placate you. I would like to drag some of them down to the leukaemia wards. Some of the things they say, calling people hysterical and ignorant, and saying that the fear of leukaemia is something only in the lower social classes and women. I think anybody who has seen what the children go through couldn't possibly say something like that.

'I also get angry with people in the area who believe the industry is responsible for a lot of bad things but don't do anything about it or don't act on it. For years I have felt that I was one of the few who dared speak out. Having a child with leukaemia and actually blaming Sellafield. I felt angry that people didn't even demand more research until YTV came along.'

Janine described the harrowing treatment the children have to go through. 'The treatment is basically geared on the chemo-therapy, to attack the immune cells which are being reproduced at different stages of their development. They start with a very high intensive course of chemotherapy which lasts about three weeks. The little ones have a tube which gets fed into a vein in their neck through which the drugs can be put at regular intervals. The older ones have a permanent drip into their arm. They are on a per-manent sort of saline solution, through which the drugs are put. There are various drugs which they get at various times when they get injections. The drugs make them very sick. After this intensive three-week treatment they have a period of radiation treatment, where their skull and spine get irradiated for two weeks and they lose their hair. They go through a sleepy period about six weeks after the radiation. All the time they are on treatment their immunity is so low that an infection is a potential killer. Some of the side effects of some of the drugs are horrendous. There is a particular one which after the treatment gives them terrible cramps in their legs. I know it was the case with Lee. Some of the other drugs give them terrible stomach aches, so bad at some stage of the initial treatment they thought Lee had appendicitis on top of everything else, which was luckily not the case. Then they get steroids to counteract the effects of some of these drastic drugs. They have another drug which is really horrendous stuff. If, by any chance they don't hit the vein and it gets into the muscle it attacks the nerve system. Lee had an unlucky do like that and he couldn't use his arm for weeks and weeks. With the steroids some kids would go wild and want to eat the wildest things, others became very bad tempered. Others can't take it at all and develop dia-betes. Thrush, if they get thrush it can spread through their sys-tem, not just to their mouth, but can get in the lungs. It's all because their immune system is so shot up.'

There are some people who have strong views on Sellafield who are not attached to either the industry or the campaigning groups. One of these people is Professor Keith Boddy who is the radiation advisor to the Northern Regional Health Authority. Professor Boddy was keen to have it stressed how independent he is of any particular group or organisation, 'Sitting in the middle in working for the health service, I have no axe to grind for BNFL which, in a sense, distracts me from my main functions of running a medical physics department. I have no economic axe to grind and I have no income whatsoever that relates to that industry. Because of the time it takes to do the work on Sellafield it's more of a hindrance than a help to me personally.

'I have been critical of BNFL. I am equally critical of anti-nuclear groups who also do not present the whole picture. It's a very difficult tightrope to walk. My primary concern is the health of the people of my region.'

Keith Boddy is not well known for publicly condemning the industry, as he prefers to work through the Environmental Sub-Committee of the Local Liaison Committee of which he is chairman, a position to which he is elected by councillors and other people. It is not given to him by BNFL. 'I think over the years the discharges in the '70s were higher than they need have been and I think that the reduction to the kind of levels we have now was by no means inappropriate. It's fairly demonstrable that the radiation doses associated with the levels which are being discharged now are comparatively small for the general public compared to exposure from national background and medical exposures.'

Professor Boddy believes radiation exposure from Sellafield has to be considered in relation to other sources of radiation. 'If you look at the group which is most highly exposed, the "critical" group who will have the maximum exposure due to eating large amounts of winkles, then the dose for 1987 was 0.33 mSv. That radiation exposure, for the eight people thought to be most exposed from Sellafield's discharges, can be compared with the radiation dose due to natural background in parts of Devon and Cornwall. The winkle-eater's dose is one-sixtieth of the dose to 60,000 people in Devon and Cornwall, who are at the action level of 20 mSv due to radon and its daughter products. The radiation dose to the winkle eaters is also quite small compared to the average dose from medical exposure throughout the country. The average West Cumbrian dose is very small indeed, roughly equivalent to spending three hours in Devon and Cornwall where the natural background is at the action level. But even the highest levels there only give you a risk that's about the same as drinking half a teaspoon of wine per week.

'The actual limit for radon in houses is 20 mSv. The limit for nuclear workers is 50 mSv, with an average exposure of about

7.5 mSv. There are about 6,000 people in Devon and Cornwall living with a constant dose that is greater than is permitted for occupational workers. The average background dose in the UK is 2 mSv, which we can't avoid, so even 0.33 mSv is still small compared to that.'

Professor Boddy believes that, 'If you want to spend money in the most sensible fashion then it should be to reduce the radon in the homes in Devon and Cornwall, which could be done relatively easily for about £500–£1,000 per house. If you've got to prioritise where to focus your attention on radiation exposure of the general public then that's the first place you'd go to, because those exposures are so much higher than the eight winkle eaters in West Cumbria and certainly far, far greater than for the average West Cumbrian exposure.

'Background doses can vary between 1–100 mSv. From medical sources, the dose can range from zero, if you have no X-rays, increasing with the number of examinations, diagnoses and therapy. The average from nuclear discharges is 0.3 mSv for eight winkle eaters. Because of natural background in South Western England, 600,000 are being exposed to more than 5 mSv. You'd save more people from radiation exposure if you spent money on reducing radon exposure.' Is it reasonable to expect BNFL to spend money on Devon and Cornwall, even though there are large radiation exposures from natural sources to some people there? After all BNFL has no facilities in either of those counties.

Professor Boddy was particularly critical of the money that is going into the further reduction of alpha discharges from Sellafield. 'We in medicine are by far the biggest source of exposure to the general public from artificial sources. We know that by changing components in X-ray systems we can make a very substantial reduction in the dose to the general public. If you think about the average then this would be a far better investment to use the £150 million that BNFL are spending on reducing alpha discharges.

'The public pressure to spend that money is different and that's why it's important that anti-nuclear groups, the industry and especially people in the health service say to the public what are the levels of exposure. Radon has always been released and can be controlled and people are being exposed at far higher doses than they need be.

'I think environmental groups are vital in that they are able to focus on a large number of issues. Many of them have the resources and the time to be able to look at those environmental issues. But it is absolutely essential that they, as the people in the middle ground, should give the public the totality of the facts, not just a blinkered approach to it. It's vital environmental groups don't fall into the same trap the industry has fallen into of saying well this is what these exposures are and not provide any proper perspectives.

'I've been critical of the way there's been so much secrecy in the industry and that material was presented only for experts. They took the view that if Joe Public wants to know about it what we've got to to do is educate Joe Public up to this kind of level. I think that's entirely wrong because it takes many years of experience of radiation protection. It's important the industry does the same; it takes me a great deal of effort to express, for the liaison committee, what are the exposures and what are they in terms they can understand. I've been criticised by some people that I'm prostituting my science.'

The critical group in Cumbria once used to get 3.65 mSv per annum from fish and shellfish eating alone. In fact the largest impact in reducing radiation exposure in Cumbria came not because of sea discharge reduction technology, but because people eat a lot less sea food now.

Professor Boddy did touch on the matter of whose money BNFL is spending, although he was not as forthcoming as he could have been, not for lack of honesty, but because like many others he fears the pitfalls of what he sees as the political arena. 'If you and I as taxpayers are putting money into the nuclear industry there should be no reason why that money, belonging to you and me, could not be diverted into the areas where this is best going to be spent in terms of radiation exposures. Supposing BNFL made a massive profit and we are the shareholders and we have some say in how that money is going to be spent. Are you and I, as members of the public, not going to say that by far the biggest exposures are in Devon and Cornwall, let's put money into there or into medicine?'

There is another way of looking at this. The NRPB does state that for any given dose of radiation the exposure must be justified in terms of the practice giving rise to the dose providing a positive net benefit. If reprocessing in economic, energy and environmental terms gives no benefit then radiation doses cannot be justified. Therefore, Professor Boddy was asked what he saw as the benefits of reprocessing spent nuclear fuel? Once again, he felt unable to answer as he did not want to step outside his professional field.

'That's not an area in which I'm an expert. My expertise relates to radiation protection of the public within my region. Whether or not nuclear power continues is a matter of indifference to me at my age. There is going to be enough power to last for the rest of my lifetime, therefore it's my children who can worry about what form and what source of the electricity power is going to be best. I don't want to bequeath to them a situation in which there's no power.

'Whether it's worth reprocessing fuel gets into a question of economics, areas in which I'm not an expert. I do not believe my opinion on those issues is worth any more than anybody's else's. Radiation exposures and the perspectives on that is the area where I have independent expertise.' Professor Boddy is not alone in not wanting to answer questions outside his own field of work. Indeed, many scientists are in the same position. Yet if he feels that nuclear power is not damaging in terms of health impact, would he not promote that over other energy sources?

He was adamant about his views on the health impact, so far, of Sellafield's discharges in terms of their radioactivity. 'A thing that concerns me, is the preoccupation with radiation when in fact the COMARE report and the Black Report indicate that the levels of exposure cannot account for the levels of leukaemias in children. If people insist on saying that radiation must be the sole cause and other things are not looked at then we're missing a vital opportunity to find out what might be the causes of any additional childhood leukaemias.

'Three independent expert committees and people like Sir Richard Doll, who must be respected, have said the radiation exposures just do not tie up with this. Therefore the more leukaemias one finds the less likely it is that radiation from the discharges is going to be the cause.'

The argument that Boddy was referring to was refuted by Dr

Robin Russell-Jones, best known as the chairman of the very successful lead-free petrol campaign. If the radiation doses resulting from Sellafield were too low to have caused the leukaemias which occurred then the more leukaemias the less Sellafield was to blame. Russell-Jones points out that this is patently not tenable as the more leukaemias which arise in that area mean that they are so much more linked to that specific locality an area heavily polluted by an industry linked with leukaemias and cancers. Russell-Jones also put forward another argument to rebut distancing of Sellafield from the leukaemias in Seascale. He called this the 'flat earth theory'. It was once thought the earth was flat. Subsequent observations proved otherwise. The same with Sellafield's discharges. The theory was that there would be no ill-health effect from Sellafield. However, observations among the local population strongly indicate the contrary. As Russell-Jones said, 'If the theory doesn't prove the facts, change the theory'. For BNFL that would mean admitting that radiation is more damaging than they once thought. The above points were put to Sir Douglas Black who remarked that 'Common sense dictates that they should be connected, but common sense is not science.' (g 12.9.84).

Estimates of the possible health damage from the discharges have been accepted by the nuclear industry. In his report on the sea discharges Peter Taylor of PERG used the calculations of the International Commission on Radiological Protection to give a figure for health damage. For Sellafield it is calculated that the discharge is causing 2–3 fatal cancers, 2–3 non-fatal cancers, 2–3 genetic defects and 2–3 non-genetic defects every year. Those estimates were given under the old radiation risks estimates. The figures could now be increased three or five fold. Some scientists would even put the figures at ten times higher. There is also an estimate of the amount of money it costs to deal with health effects of radiation. Using standards set by the Environmental Protection Agency of the United States the Sellafield discharges are believed to cost £190 million to the European and United Kingdom health services so far.

However, Boddy is not totally dismissive of any link. 'If you say is it due to the plant then yes, it might well be due to the plant, but not associated with the discharges or radiation. There has been work which suggested that the grouping of new populations together is one reason why on a virus theory you will have a higher incidence of leukaemias. That has been demonstrated not just around nuclear installations, but in new towns which have nothing to do with them.'

However, as Sir Richard Doll has pointed out, the virus theory does not hold up very well. He wrote and told us: 'I can reassure you completely about the risk of a child with leukaemia being infectious. There are several sorts of cancer that are now known to be caused, in part, by viruses, including one type of leukaemia which is rare in England and principally affects adults. None of them can be 'caught' by contact with a patient. Infection with these viruses often causes no symptoms at all, or may cause an influenza-like illness and spread, when it occurs, is during the early stages of infection from people who are not suffering from cancer. If the increase of childhood leukaemia which occurred in Cumbria over the last twenty years was due to a viral infection it is likely to have been because of changes in the population that occurred in this period and it is very unlikely that any similar excess will occur in the future.

'I am personally far from convinced that a virus plays any part in the production of childhood leukaemia in this country, but the idea is scientifically attractive, not only because many leukaemias in animals are caused by viruses but also because it could explain some of the epidemiological findings.'

Doll added in his letter, 'Only two factors are firmly established as causes of childhood leukaemia: namely ionising radiation and some of the drugs used in the treatment of or to facilitate organ transplantation. A great deal is known about the former from past studies which have shown that about five per cent of cases have been caused by X-ray examination of the mother's abdomen during pregnancy, but the doses that have done this, though small in themselves, are larger in comparison with the doses that people have received from natural radiation and the much smaller amounts from nuclear waste. We know the latter are very small because measurements have been made on people exposed to it which show that the amount of radioactive material absorbed is, if anything, less than the amount estimated from the reported discharges.' (letter 16.5.89).

Over the last few years the theory that a virus is the cause of the

Seascale leukaemias has been put about by a number of people. However, as Barrie Walker explained, this is all too easy a trap to fall into: 'The recent statements that there may be a virus causing leukaemia in children does raise funny implications. Anybody who's got leukaemia, if you believe in viral aetiology, I guess you'd better keep away from them. That would be a very straightforward simplistic interpretation wouldn't it, but it's not quite as simple as that. It's to do with alternation of immune states after exposure to lots of different viruses. If you believe the viral study, you then believe leukaemias should occur in the indigenous population and certainly that's not the case. It's happening in the children of incomers. I'm not terribly convinced about this theory. Some people certainly think that a virus may be one of the contributory factors to leukaemia. I don't think anybody would dispute that. But whether you need to use their peculiar logic to support that is another matter. Lots of people believe it may be virus and radiation combined. The theory at the moment is a virus or chemical effect – either an organic solvent or possibly the chemical effect of plutonium itself. Nobody's really looked at what it will do chemically as opposed to radiologically. The lymphomas we are seeing now, well, they've got a long incubation period and perhaps they are linked with things that have happened in the past.'

Janine, as a mother of a son with leukaemia, was more worried over the social implications of the virus theory: 'I don't know whether people have really thought over the implications. We know it is not "catching". The cases seem to be quite unconnected, although they occur in a particular area. Yet they persist in saying it is a virus without having identified a virus, they are just speculating. I think the social implications of a virus are very serious. The kids have a lot to cope with, without the fear of other people wanting to stay away from them. They have come a long way in allaying the fear of cancer, now to imply it might be infectious is getting the whole thing back and just creates more problems for the kids who have it.'

Professor Boddy did point to newer research which suggested causes other than radiation, but still involving industrial processes in some way. 'There has been some work which shows that in the offspring of parents exposed to organic solvents, or insecticides and pesticides, there's an excess of leukaemias. The World Health

Report shows an excess of cancer amongst painters exposed to solvent-based paints. There's a suggestion of an excess of leukaemias amongst their children. That's nothing to do with radiation, but the plants at Dounreay and Sellafield, perhaps elsewhere, certainly involve handling solvents. It is said why look for some other cause when there is an obvious one? But what if the obvious one doesn't fit some preconceived idea? I'm not saying a virus is the cause, I'm saying there is a multiplicity of causes.

'The vital thing is that minds should be open rather than saying there is only one cause, let's forget about others.'

CHAPTER
9

Did you ever expect a corporation to have a conscience when it has no soul to be damned and no body to be kicked?
Edward Thurlow

If the YTV programme had dealt BNFL a body-blow, then the next piece of publicity about Sellafield was to send them reeling. The 'accidental' release into the Irish Sea, in November 1983, of a very radioactive slick proved a great embarrassment. The slick was a layer of 'crud' made up of purex, the cleaner used in shutdown operations to remove excess radioactive material from various parts of the reprocessing machinery. This crud is usually kept on site as it is too radioactive to go out to sea. The accidental part of the 1983 fiasco was that this material had actually got into the sea tanks. Few people realise that the decision to discharge was quite deliberate.

Local feeling on the state of the beaches was already running high because of YTV's film. When we took the protest train to London, on 12th November, with five hundred Cumbrians on board, we raised the stakes further. We dumped a dustbin full of radioactive mud on Whitehall, opposite the entrance to 10 Downing Street. The effect was electrifying. Half of Whitehall was blocked off and a special chemical incidents van was sent to take the mud away. The authorities' reaction was hardly in keeping with claims that this publicly accessible silt was safe. The silt had come from the mouth of the Drigg stream outlet, one of the most contaminated spots on the coast. The gamma radiation readings alone were 100 times background. We were, of course, accused by a Department of Environment spokesman of doctoring the mud we had dumped. I wonder where he thought we got the caesium and plutonium which was in it?

Greenpeace had decided, prior to the YTV programme, to block the Sellafield pipeline. On 14th November 1983 we met up with Greenpeace workers in Ravenglass. They told us that in July of that year they had placed a buoy at the end of the pipeline and in November they had gone back to check it was still there. They had two Geiger counters on board their dinghy. When they reached the marker buoy, one Geiger counter soared off-scale and the other was almost mute. They headed quickly back to shore, but they were mystified. They thought that water had possibly leaked into the counter which was giving the high readings. I had often measured radioactivity levels around Sellafield, Drigg and Ravenglass and I was well acquainted with the areas of highest readings. It simply did not occur to me that the reading could be genuine. I told them not to worry and that the Geiger counter was probably broken.

Immediately after this meeting three of the Greenpeace people came with Joe Thompson and myself to Silloth, near Maryport, for a debate with BNFL. The two BNFL speakers were Les Tuley, head of Sellafield's information department (who was also Chairman of the Education Committee for Cumbria at the time) and his colleague Dr Steven Jones, head of environmental protection at Sellafield. Throughout the meeting neither of the men mentioned that there had been a major leak from the plant, which had started on Friday the 11th. Yet there they were sitting in a crowded school in a fishing town. All the way to Maryport and all the way back we sat in a van with the dinghies and other contaminated equipment. Two of the Greenpeace crew sat in the back of the van on top of the gear.

As soon as the dinghies were brought back to London Greenpeace contacted the NRPB, whose monitoring confirmed the high levels of radiation we had found on the beach at Ravenglass. Those who were there said the NRPB were, initially, as mystified as everyone else as to why there were such high readings.

For nine days, the authorities made no attempt to warn the public who used the sea or the shore. The Greenpeace divers who went down to block the pipe some eight days later at least had some idea that they might get contaminated. They wore gloves, they were cleaned when they got back on-board ship. But the fishermen who had been trawling off the pipeline remained in ignorance.

Our anger and concern was exemplified when a local fisherman wrote to the newspapers saying that he was one of several anglers who took advantage of the very calm seas on 18th November to do a spot of fishing. He was there again the next day.

That fisherman wanted to know why the local anglers or the people who used the beaches on Saturday were not warned. He also raised a question much asked in the days immediately following the accident – why was no effort made to find those who did use the beaches on those days?

It was a sad letter, because it reflected the anguish of many people in the area. The last paragraph spoke volumes: 'When I moved to Seascale I did so because of the excellent countryside, the friendly people and above all its superb beach. I still love the area, but for three months I have been denied access to the beach and, whatever the arguments, there is no denying BNFL are responsible for that. So to those readers who are worried about the economy and tourism I say don't blame the media, Greenpeace or the Department of Environment. The sooner BNFL can learn to come clean on these matters the sooner we will all have our confidence in them restored.' (w/n 15.3.84).

In the days immediately after NRPB monitors checked the contaminated Greenpeace dinghies BNFL tried to play things down. On Sunday 20th pieces of seaweed and flotsam found on Seascale beach were monitored and found to be up to 1,000 times background levels for gamma and beta radiation. A public warning was given to avoid using the beach if possible. I had arrived in Seascale on the Sunday evening when the Greenpeace ship arrived to start the blocking of the pipeline. The beach was 'reopened' on the Monday morning. It stayed open until the evening of Thursday 24th, when the rate of highly contaminated objects coming on shore was such that the Department of the Environment said that people should 'avoid all unnecessary uses of the beaches until stated otherwise'. In the period between the 'bans' up to eighty press and media people had been on those beaches following the Greenpeace action.

The official caution meant little, for throughout the whole six months of the closure no official warning notices were posted on Cumbrian beaches. The area chosen was arbitrary, for contaminated seaweed was found beyond the boundary of the specified area both north and south. The absurdity of the beach ban was all too clear in the instructions given to people. For example to 'avoid unnecessary use of the beach' was open to misinterpretation. What was classed as 'unnecessary use'? Fishermen were left to balance the risks of radiation exposure against loss of income.

The NRPB admitted that some of the articles that could be found might be very contaminated. The fishermen of Ravenglass, and those who owned small boats, were treated to a special presentation by the Department of the Environment. They were told clothing was to be washed with sea water to prevent possible contaminated mud drying off and being taken on board boats or into cars and homes. During the time this advice was being given the beach was still open to public use. The Ministry of Agriculture, Fisheries and Food was quick to emphasise that no contamination above 'normal' had been found, but still said that people should wear boots on the beach and heavy duty gloves when handling mooring tackle.

The impression given was that it would be improbable that a member of the public would come into contact with a very radioactive piece of flotsam. Communications between the experts was not good. Professor Boddy told local press at the start of the beach ban that he believed it was safe to go on the beaches (w/n 15.12.83). He said it would be dangerous only if someone held a contaminated article for a long period of time. Yet it was revealed at the subsequent court case that levels of up to 27 rems per hour had been found on some objects by the NRPB. In that case the yearly dose for beta radiation would be reached in eleven minutes! (w/n July 85). Keith Boddy did say that 'the chance of finding something radioactive from the slick is somewhere around one in 10 million' (w/n 17.5.84).

Les Tuley was, throughout this time, a man with many worries. As one of the heads of BNFL media relations he was in a flat spin over what to do next. As a politician he was heartily embarrassed, especially in his role as Chairman of the Education Committee. In January 1984 a new head teacher for Barrow's College of Further Education decided to turn down the post which had been offered him as his family was too worried about the move (e/m 13.1.84). Applicants for jobs in Workington and Egremont also withdrew. Tuley blamed the YTV programme for these problems (w/n 15.12.83).

In April 1984 a German school cancelled a visit altogether because of fears of the plant and the effect it might have. The children were to stay with Wyndham School pupils. Tuley was a governor of Wyndham School when this happened (w/n 18.4.84). All the while BNFL were making renewed efforts to get people to visit the exhibition centre.

Tuley was called on to answer why the local schools on Walney Island, in Barrow, had been issued with potassium iodate tablets. The tablets, of course, were there in case the 'unthinkable' happened, that is a large release of radioactivity from a nuclear submarine in Barrow. Wearing both his BNFL hat and his education hat Tuley said that this was simply a wise precaution and 'perfectly normal and reasonable'.

The Sellafield unions were not quiet throughout all of this. They did criticise the management for their mishandling of the accident. They were unhappy with the explanation given for the slick being released. In a statement to the press Bill Maxwell said, 'We met senior management and the Works General Manager and they gave their story as to what had happened.' Bill Maxwell added, 'The shop floor may not accept in total their story. We in the unions want a strong, secure industry, but we certainly do not want the beach contaminated. Safety is our paramount concern.' (w/n 24.11.83).

The 900 AEU members on site passed a vote of no confidence in the management. A union spokesman said, 'We have no confidence in the company for allowing these beaches to be contaminated. The management are responsible for the contamination because they are responsible for the plant operational procedures. We have no say in these at all.'

Criticism of the company was not restricted to the blue-collar workers. The white-collar IPCS said the management was 'looking for scapegoats' after the accident. Bill Brett, Assistant General Secretary of the IPCS, said, 'We welcome the wide-ranging improvements in safety procedures which are being implemented, but utterly deplore the company's unwarranted decisions to take disiplinary action against a few individual managers when in our view there was clear evidence that company's operating instructions had not been breached by staff. A few individuals are being made scapegoats for inadequate procedures throughout the company.' (w/n 23.2.84). It was well known that the unions were fighting to avoid blame falling on the workforce. The reason is quite plain. If they were to take the blame now they would always take the blame and, after all, they were not solely responsible for the accident. Bad operating instructions, faulty pipework and out-moded procedures were just as much to blame.

Or were they? The unions had good reason to worry that some of their members might be collared. A printed note which outlined the set rules for cleaning out the tanks during shutdown had been amended by hand. On the section dealing with the recovery of solvent (that is the actual crud that went to sea) someone had written, 'for this shutdown it is proposed not to float off and recover solvent higher activity waste'. This meant the crud which formed the slick would not be kept on site. Whoever had changed the rules, in their own handwriting, was obviously in big trouble. More to the point, whoever had followed the instructions without questioning them was an accomplice. Why did those workers who initially wanted to send the slick out to sea then change their minds and try to recover it? Were they caught in the act?

It was the act of sending the crud back into the plant, for storage in the right tank, that forced the decision to release the slick. Workers sent to deal with it could not go near the pipework as it was so radioactive. The NII confirmed that this had happened. The radioactivity was so great that it had penetrated the extra thick concrete and lead shielding around the tanks and pipework (w/n 15.12.83). Radiation badges were exposed to so much radia-tion that they turned black. At the 1985 trial, health physicist William Lee told of how he stood behind John Bellfield as he attempted to turn the valve which would send the solvent out to sea. As he did so Lee's radiation monitor went off-scale and he shouted at Bellfield to leave. They did not wait to check radiation levels (w/n fourth week of trial July 1985). So, it was in order to protect the workers that the discharge was, eventually, given the go-ahead.

At the trial the NII said that chemicals could have been used to lessen the amount of radioactivity which had gone to sea, or that efforts could have been made to put in pipework to reroute the discharge after the first attempts had failed.

Perhaps one reason for the plant not being shut down whilst the trouble with the crud was sorted, was because a shutdown could have cost £1 million per day to the company (w/n 18.7.85). The company estimated it would have taken sixteen weeks to build alternative piping, at a cost of £400,000. Given the £1 million a day price tag the overall cost, had they stopped reprocessing, would have been £112 million. Would this actually have been more expensive than the legal action and all the bad publicity? Who knows.

The trial was another 'first' for BNFL as it was the first time a public utility in England had ever been taken to court on criminal charges. The company was found guilty on four counts. They were fined £10,000. Greenpeace was fined £50,000 for trying to block the pipeline from Sellafield.

BNFL carried out a 'spring clean' of the beaches. Afterwards they said, 'The important thing is that we have not found any radioactivity amongst the forty lorry loads of debris that have been taken off the beaches since Thursday.' (w/n 29.3.84). That's because most of it was still on the beaches or in the sea. Of the 4,000 curies released it is estimated that less than one-tenth of a curie was found on contaminated articles retrieved on the beach (w/n 23.8.84).

In taking the decision to discharge the slick to sea BNFL may well have saved themselves money, but they caused other businesses to lose out. Immediately after the trial it was disclosed that several west coast businesses had hired solicitors to consider cases of compensation. Like the Merlins, these people were seeking to prove damage to property via loss of earnings. In fact in 1984 a number of businesses were hit very badly, with some claiming losses of up to 60 per cent. In February the Smugglers Cove group of hotels asked BNFL for £3,000 compensation for the fourteen-strong group to cover the cost of advertising which they said was wasted because of the bad publicity.

The effects of the accident were to be felt for years. David Inwood bought his £70,000 North Villa Hotel in Seascale only a few months before the accident. Speaking to the *Guardian* in 1986 he admitted that in the three years in-between not one holiday maker had stayed at his place. He was attempting to sell up, but the property was valued at only £55,000. He had tried to get an outside job, but had failed. In the same article the manager of the

Scawfell Hotel, Michael Magee, said that at Easter 1986 his seventy bedroom hotel had only ten rooms full. His rooms were normally taken with BNFL contractors or businessmen. He used to get coach loads of visitors on mystery tours from Keswick. 'But when they found out the mystery was Seascale they were not very pleased. Now no one comes at all.'

In March 1984 BNFL told Millom hoteliers that the beaches were safe. Paul Wilson, BNFL PR, told a meeting, 'Last November there was an abnormal release from Sellafield. It has never happened before and will never happen again.' (e/m 30.3.84).

At the May 1984 meeting of the Sellafield Local Liaison Committee, the Windscale Works Manager, John Donoghue, was asked if such a leak could have occurred before. He told a dismayed audience, 'I can't give a 100 per cent guarantee that there hasn't been such material on the beach previously.' (w/n 10.5.84).

Few, if any, of the public knew that contaminated material had been found from Maryport in the north to Walney beach in the south, (g. 10.3.84) far beyond the designated ban in force at the time. Contaminated material was also still being found months after the beach ban was lifted, albeit at a much lower level.

BNFL on occasion do things designed to test the patience of local people. In July 1984, during the Cumbrian leg of the 1984 Three Peaks race, a crowd had gathered on the beach at Ravenglass, where the competitors land before they run to Scawfell. They were obviously unperturbed by the beach ban. Who should show up in the middle of all of this but several BNFL monitors?

One section of the community that is always hit by bad publicity from Sellafield is the fishermen. Perhaps none has been hit as badly as Paul Pederson, from Ravenglass. Along with his son, also called Paul, he fishes daily for flat fish from around the mouth of the Ravenglass estuary. Throughout the war he had lived at Whitehaven and his trawler was not seconded, because he was Danish born and classified as an 'alien'. However, he was well aware of the privilege of being allowed to carry on his livelihood whilst those around had to make sacrifices for the war. He helped in his own way by taking his catches to the beleagured Isle of Man, where his fish were so desperately needed he had to have a police escort to land them! Pederson's wife died with stomach cancer when they lived at Whitehaven, a tragedy which precipitated his move to Ravenglass. In 1976 he admitted that he had seen cod with 'burnt eyes' (g 16.10.76), but insisted that this was due to the detergent discharged from Marchon. He was vociferous in his condemnation of YTV after this film. Pederson said that until then his business attracted some forty or fifty customers a day from April to November. He said that 'marine life in the estuary was, "the healthiest in Europe". The rubbish put out in that programme has knocked hell out of my business. We've never had a good living over the years, but it looks impossible now. In the first two days after the programme we didn't have a single customer. At other times my customers have come back after the fuss has died down, but I don't think they will come back this time. We've written a strong letter of complaint to YTV and if we don't get a satisfactory reply then we'll sue them.' (w/n 10.11.83). He told a German film crew, 'The house over there on the corner is only half finished and you can't find a buyer. Over there is another. They are already on offer much cheaper, but despite this they can't get rid of them. The people are so afraid I'd rather not be able to sell my house, I mean, I could, but I'd practically have to give it away.'

Paul Pederson junior said, 'I had a very good little business here, but it is down by about 60 per cent. I will give it another month and if it doesn't pick up I will pack it in. I have been offered a job by BNFL, but I have been a fisherman all my life and somehow I can't see myself sitting in an office.' (sun tel 19.2.84).

In August 1984, in order to 'prove' how safe the local beaches were, the Junior Energy Minister Giles Shaw took an early morning dip off the Seascale beach. Local shopkeepers were not impressed, as the dip had taken place at 7.30 a.m. on an empty beach.

For the majority of people there was no comfort in being caught up between Sellafield and the environmental lobby. In 1986 local hoteliers were still complaining of losing money over Sellafield. The Greenpeace ship, the Sirius, had returned to the area to highlight Sellafield's continuing discharges. Joe Walsh, the manager of the Scawfell Hotel, said, 'I blame the bad press on BNFL and Greenpeace has not helped. Their ship should have been blown out of the sea. It's not helping anything to do with Seascale.' (w/n 3.4.86).

As someone who lived right next to the plant, and as a regular beach user, Dorothy Bateman admitted that she thought BNFL should have told people about the accident. The company's attitude over the release was the final straw for her. 'The weekend immediately after the accident I took a walk down to the beach. I would often walk past the plant and the police Land Rover would show up. Because we lived next to the plant they knew me and we usually acknowledged each other. Actually I've never minded the policing of the fence, I applaud it as a job well done. But that Sunday it was one Land Rover after another following me down to the beach and when I got there there were police all over. I used to get things from the beach, dog-whelk purse, starfish, or feathers, anything unusual for the nature table at school because at that time I was a primary school teacher. Luckily that Sunday it became dusk quick and I left before I picked anything up. When I got back I told Walker that I thought the police were expecting some protesters. It was not until the next Sunday we heard a BNFL PR man on the radio saying there'd been a slight spillage, but nothing to worry about. It was a "brush and shovel" job and it would soon be cleaned up. That was the first we'd heard of it.

'I was so angry that I hadn't been warned not to go on the beach that I wrote to the factory and asked for an explanation as to why I wasn't stopped. Had I known there was such a serious accident I wouldn't have gone. It was arranged that someone would come and see us. Dr Jones (head of Sellafield's environmental protection department) came to see us and he told us only 600 curies had gone out into the sea from that tank and they'd recovered the rest. The main thing he was trying to tell us was we shouldn't be worrying about it. He told us it could come out in the inquiry.

'When we started asking him questions he was surprised. Several times he didn't know what to answer with. He didn't seem to know what had happened, how it had happened or why it had happened or anything about it.

'I read the proceedings of the court case and at least 4,600 curies had gone out, not 600, as was originally said. We seemed to learn of all the accidents from the TV. They probably didn't tell us as they would see it as "frightening the natives". I don't believe anything they say now.'

Dorothy was not the kind of woman to be easily pacified by BNFL. She had her own plans. 'After the beach incident I was so annoyed that they wouldn't put signs up to warn people. They kept saying people already knew about it. Anyway, I put up a sign saying "Danger 5000 counts on beach". All the buses going into the works were passing this each day. Eventually Walker was called in by his boss, he still worked at Sellafield at this time, and he was asked to ask me to take the signs down because everybody knew what the situation was. Walker said he wouldn't because he didn't think the beaches were safe and that he would take them down when he was satisfied things were OK. Then the usual happened, we got a notice from the local council asking if we had planning permission for the sign and if not we would be charged £300 for breaking the rules! While those signs were up a number of walkers knocked on our door. When we explained the situation to them they were angry that they had walked on the beach without being warned.'

During the summer after the leak the BNFL management were all shown having a barbecue of locally caught sea fish on the beach at Silecroft. The usual pictures appeared in local papers. Walker, Dorothy's husband, had his own biting criticism of that action: 'When the circus begins to lose its appeal they wheel out the clowns. That's what I felt when I saw that management stunt.'

It was not just the accident that upset the Batemans. The YTV documentary had shocked them, but they were not completely surprised. 'We'd always speculated about the effects of Sellafield. We'd noticed too many young people were dying from cancer and other illnesses for it to be wholesome and we began to worry. In 1981 we went to the Low Church and looked at all the headstones and we were horrified to find how many young people had been buried there who lived in the vicinity of the plant. In an area about one and a half miles round there were connections to about thirty-five to forty people who had died. Some were friends, who'd lived quite close. The same applied when we went to Gosforth church-yard, there again there were quite a number of people who'd died very young. It's amazing the number of people who died early at the old pre-fabs near us and at Calderbridge and Beckermet village.' A married couple from a farm that adjoined the Batemans' place both died of cancer a year after they moved from their farm.

Having found the high rate of deaths in young people how did the Batemans feel? 'We felt trapped, what do you do about a situation like that? We hadn't a choice. We could have packed up our jobs and gone where? We weren't free, we felt rather lost. I think if most people were honest they would admit they felt something was amiss, but they felt helpless. What can we do about it? A big industry like this. We're just a little cog and people just become resigned to it.'

At the time 80 per cent of the houses in Seascale were built for and were owned by BNFL and its predecessors. Only now is there a policy of selling off the property to the tenants. This might, in some way, explain the silence that has lingered over Sellafield, that and the fear that your son, or husband, or next-door neighbour could be working at the plant which caused your child's death.

For Walker and Dorothy the YTV programme confirmed their worst fears, 'When we watched the YTV programme we realised even from that moment that a lot of what was being said we thought was correct. We'd already seen things to make us suspicious. With bringing up a family just over the fence we were worried. We'd heard on the grapevine of one or two children with cancer, but not that many.

'We worry about our three children, even though they are now grown up and living away from Cumbria. Of course we worry. They are all married now and we hope and pray that their children will be all right when they come to have them. Some years ago a senior nuclear physicist advised us not to eat or drink the local meat, vegetables and milk. Since then we've made it our business not to. If a young woman came to me now and said she was considering moving to Seascale I would tell her not to. There's no future in West Cumbria, not even for the nuclear industry and certainly not for the likes of farmers. They blame the leukaemias and cancers on sewage, viruses, anything but Sellafield. But before 1950 such illness were very rare in that area. As for the beach, they say people stay away because of the sewage. Yet in the mid-70s there was a terrible problem with sewage on Seascale beach and yet they were packed in. Now, even though they have a longer sewage outfall pipe, the beaches are empty even on the best of days.'

Walker thinks that dishonesty is the only thing that has allowed Sellafield to come about. 'Quite honestly I don't think the authorities could tell people the truth. Had they told people the truth from the beginning, of the hazards and potential hazards, it would never have got off the ground. We could have had a tourist industry along that lovely coast, it would have provided as many, if not more, jobs than Sellafield, without all the hazards and waste and danger. They blotted the landscape and contaminated the environment. What they've done to West Cumbria is wicked. They've ruined it forever. How many years is it going to take to go – even if they stopped the discharges tomorrow? I can't understand Copeland and the Cumbria councillors allowing it to go ahead.'

Walker firmly believes the local population could have done more for itself. 'Everybody says that your local councillors, you put them there, if you're not satisfied with them you get them out. But in our situation there's so many councillors working on the site that it's one big happy family. They're too close to see the problems. When you look at what happens in other areas both here and abroad, when nuclear waste is mentioned, people just refuse it. The jobs argument doesn't wash with them. I think that they could have employed more people if the same amount of investment had gone into other industries. I think our local MP Jack Cunningham could have helped us more. He should have been sticking his neck out for the welfare of West Cumbria, not just Sellafield. Not jobs that no other county will have, but good jobs. Not just the dead end ones. I think he should live in Copeland.'

Dorothy is normally a calm, quiet woman, but her belief in what Sellafield has done makes her angry. 'I don't see any gain for Cumbria, in having the plant. In fact it is a debit. Our countryside and sea are polluted. The off-comers have spoilt the little villages and taken the best paid jobs. It will be us that'll be left to clear up the mess after they've gone and left it all behind. Other areas must think how silly and foolish the Cumbrians are. They must be laughing at us. When you talk to them they can't understand why we put up with it. The industry has sweet-talked its way to expansion. For example we were promised a bypass for Egremont when THORP was being asked for. That's not being fulfilled. Now that same thing will be the promise for the nuclear waste dump they want.'

Walker was in the union at the plant. 'I'm a very strong believer in unions in all industries, but having said that I'm afraid the unions at Sellafield haven't been doing the best job. I don't think the compensation scheme is a good idea at all because if an industry's guilty then the industry should pay out fair and square. They shouldn't use a back-door method which is how I view the scheme. Anyway, an industry that's paid out the amount that BNFL has paid out is hardly innocent.'

Walker and Dorothy became worried when plans to build a plutonium incineration plant opposite the house were talked about. The company was also intending to close the end of the road and bring the perimeter fence right up to their own garden wall so they decided to up and move. After they left the house was bought by BNFL, and Walker's brother sold the rest of the farm to them. 'What could he do, no one else is interested in owning farmland around the site. There's no one living in the house now, BNFL use it for smoke practice for their fire service. The farm house is empty too. It breaks my heart to go down and see the farm as it is now. To think that generations before me nurtured and tended that farm. My family's heritage has gone.'

Since the Bateman's moved the son of another Yottenfews family which moved away had died of a brain tumour. He was sixteen years old.

Walker left Sellafield in 1988. He managed to get early retirement. For a number of years he had suffered from severe ear trouble and his health was deteriorating. He was not unhappy to leave BNFL. 'I'm very sad I spent my working life in there. But I'm even sadder when I go away and people ask me where I used to work. I can't tell them, I avoid a direct answer. I've nothing in my life to be embarrassed about, but I'm ashamed to tell people that that is where I worked for twenty-six years of my life.'

CHAPTER

10

Mourn not the dead in the cool earth lie,
Ashes to Ashes,
Dust to Dust.
Rather mourn the apathetic throng,
The coward and the meek,
Who see the world's great wrong
And dare not speak.
Epitaph of Bram Longstaffe, former Mayor of Barrow

If the effects of Sellafield were felt only within the immediate area of the plant there is no doubt it would never have caused such controversy. As it is, the impact of accidents like 1957 and the sea discharges have meant that many places have felt the touch of Sellafield. Even if you live outside Copeland you may not necessarily remain unscathed. The people of Barrow on the Furness Peninsula are only too aware of Sellafield's close proximity.

Like many other men who were in Barrow in the 1950s, my father worked at Sellafield. He was a foreman steel erector on the site. He had already seen the hazards in other industries. Coming from a mining community in Blantyre near Glasgow he had known the toll that that industry could take in human lives. A conscript during the war, he had been placed in bomb-disposal. Like many after the war he wanted only to know peace and prosperity. He believed, as did many, that nuclear power would play a role in a better life for all. At the age of forty, in 1962, my father died on site at Sellafield. His body was taken to Whitehaven, where it was kept for two days while the post-mortem was carried out, which only served to add to my mother's distress. Although the post-mortem report said that the cause of death was a heart attack as a result of coronary thrombosis my mother has always believed that radiation might have played some part in my father's death.

Before my father had begun to work there my mother and he

171

had quarrelled over nuclear power. She well remembers one particular day when they were walking along the footpath that led beside the coal-powered power-station in Barrow. My father had worked on the site, but was full of praise for nuclear power and told her he was keen to get a job at Sellafield. She asked him not to work at the plant. Not that her fears were founded on any knowledge, just an instinctive worry over all things nuclear. My father said he would not work on a military nuclear facility. When he started as a construction worker on the Calder Hall reactor he did not know they would produce plutonium for the UK's nuclear weapons programme.

After my father's death, with four young children to look after, my mother was in no state to question the post-mortem findings. She did ask a number of people if they thought radiation could be to blame, but most people patronised her and tried to put her fears down to her grief. By this time my mother's fears were based on something more than instinct as she had seen the authorities' reaction to the fallout from the 1957 fire. At the time of the accident she was pregnant with me. She had been alerted to the contamination of the milk when her next door neighbour had rushed in asking if she had heard the police cars going around the estate telling people of the restrictions on milk. Because my mother was pregnant and because she had three other young children she was given a can of milk when she got to the shop. She recalls now how panicky people were and remarks that she would not like to see how they would react to an accident today. At the time my father was working at the British Steel plant in Barrow. He had left Sellafield because of his deteriorating health. He wanted a job nearer home. The accident shocked my father, he became angry that it had happened. He insisted that my brother and sister come home every lunch-time rather than have school meals which were possibly contaminated. He felt it was too late to take stronger action as the authorities had waited three days before admitting to the contamination.

In October 1958 my father suffered his first heart attack, which put him on the sick for twelve months. When one of his friends from Sellafield came to the house and asked him to return to work at the plant he said yes. Although he was worried he still wanted to get back to reasonably well paid work to support his family. He had never been on the sick before, he could not stand receiving benefits and the fact that the money was so little only added to his stress. My mother said she cried when he went back, not just because she did not like Sellafield, but because she felt the travelling would kill him. As I grew up I thought that what had killed my father was the fact he was a working man. I changed my mind when I read the 1985 report on those early Strontium-90 releases from the Plutonium Piles. My father was on site all the time those burst fuel cartridges were releasing radioactivity around the area. The scientists knew of the releases, they had measured increased radioactivity levels in the area around the thyroid glands of two children from Seascale.

Not long after my father had died my cousin, Kevin Barry was diagnosed as having leukaemia. He was not living in Cumbria at the time of his diagnosis, but he had been on holiday quite close to Sellafield at the time of the 1957 fire. When his parents took him in for treatment at Christies cancer hospital, they were told by the doctors that there had been a marked increase in the number of people, children in particular, that were attending the hospital from the Cumbria area. Kevin Barry was eleven years old when he died.

The thirty girls in the class of the local convent school I attended had all been born between September 1957 and August 1958. The majority of us were very young babies or foetuses at the time of the fire. Two of the teachers in the school used to call us 'Windscale' babies. Their joke was that the radioactivity made us more obstreperous than other children. But there is a serious side. When I went to see a doctor in Barrow not long after I was married he remarked on my being born not long after the fire. He asked me if I was worried about having children. I said I hadn't really thought about it, but he obviously had and he was not alone. I know many young women in this area, and along the west coast, who have had miscarriages. Almost all blame Sellafield.

It may surprise readers to learn that I was not brainwashed from an early age to hate Sellafield. I had the same sort of teenage upbringing as anybody else. In fact for six years I was married to a nuclear submariner. Living in the Naval community, especially with people who literally ate and slept next to reactors for six months of the year, gave me an insight into worries and fears not always afforded the outsider. Many of them were no different from other workers who went into careers they did not like because of economic circumstances. The submariners shared the same black humour that is prevalent in those who work with nuclear power. Lads would joke that they didn't need condoms as they were 'firing blanks' or they would point to someone and say you'd be safe near him because 'his balls have dropped off'. Talking about someone from Sellafield they would say things like 'he'll make a good striker for football, because he's got two heads and three legs'. In fact Sellafield's football team is affectionately known as the Glow Worms!

To me these people, and many others I know who work at Sellafield or building nuclear submarines, have more integrity than those who make money from buying and selling stocks and shares for armament companies and then salve their consciences by donating money to environmental groups. Even if these workers believed in the dangers of the nuclear industry, as we see them, they are guilty only of hypocrisy. How many of us are free of that sin? At best they may not believe that they are doing any harm, in which case they can be accused only of naïvety.

In January 1980 Greenpeace came to Barrow to launch their report entitled 'The Hazards Associated with the Maritime Transport of Spent Nuclear Fuel'. It started a campaign which was to have serious repercussions throughout the whole nuclear industry. Barrow is the British port for the import of most foreign spent nuclear fuel. The fuel, carried in thick containers of stainless steel and lead, known as 'flasks', is brought in on the ships of the Fisher fleet. At that time the spent fuel carriers were converted general purpose cargo ships. Prior to Greenpeace's arrival in the town, a very disturbing incident had happened with Fisher ships. The first involved the *Poole Fisher*. She had been lost in a ferocious storm in the English Channel. Thirteen people had been lost. The ship had been carrying potash at the time. The ship normally carried spent magnox fuel from Italy – the potash cargo was luckily a one-off. In another incident the chief engineer of the Pacific Swan, which was fully loaded with oxide fuel, fell downstairs drunk at a Christmas party on board the ship whilst it was out at sea. He died of head injuries.

But it was a shipboard fire which most worried Peter Taylor of the Political Ecology Research Group (PERG), who wrote the

174

report. In his report he concluded, 'a fire involving a spent nuclear fuel flask, lasting nine hours or more, could cause the release of cooling water and cracking of the flasks. Spent fuel elements would disintegrate, contaminating a wide area. An area some 50 kilometres in radius from the centre of the blaze would have to be evacuated, fishing in the Irish Sea might be banned for twenty years and tens of thousands of immediate and latent cancers would occur.' At a meeting BNFL later admitted that, if exposed to air, magnox elements (surrounded by magnesium cladding) ignite spontaneously, Thus, any crack in the flask would encourage a fire.

I had not seen the Greenpeace advert, in fact it was my work-mate Lisa who first drew my attention to it. At the time we were both working for the civil service in the Department of Employment. Lisa was interested in the issue because her brother Jamie had had his right leg amputated from the knee down when he was twelve because of a tumour in it. They had been told that radiation was to blame. The very mud that Lisa's brother would stand in to dig for fishing bait, the mud he and his friends would wade through to sit on boats to fish, was contaminated by the radioactivity discharged from Sellafield.

Many people in this area spend a lot of time on the beaches. In some of my teenage years I spent every day of the summer there. The year of the highest discharges, 1975 and the following hot summer, 1976, I spent weeks on Walney Island. When I was younger we would have winkle parties. Saturday afternoons would be spent gathering winkles, they would be soaked overnight to clean them and then they would be boiled the next day. Kids from all over the street would descend on our garden, clutching their pins with which to scoop out the winkles from their shells. When I look back now on how much seafood we all of us ate I shudder. We were living in a child's paradise. A day at the beach was free and clean and good fun. In a very working-class town with little or no money and few amenities that beach meant a lot to us. But the fish and shellfish we ate contained plutonium and caesium. Some months ago I spoke to Lisa and I was shocked to learn that Jamie's bride, who was born and raised on Walney, had died of leukaemia aged twenty-five.

Another person at the first meeting was Mavis Coward, who

lived a few streets away from Lisa. Mavis is a councillor for the North Walney ward in Barrow, where she has lived for thirty years. It was the contamination of the sea which first worried Mavis and her husband Ron. 'In 1979 the Ministry of Fisheries came to the house to ask us to take part in an experiment on diet. They knew Ron owned a boat. For a week we collected a double sample of whatever we ate and kept it in boxes. At the end of the week we took hair and nail and blood samples and we had to say how much fish we ate and how much shellfish we ate in a year. The MAFF guy was particularly interested because Ron ate fish, winkles, whelks, mussels, cockles, prawns, shrimps and I didn't eat any of them except the fish. This made us a good control household.

'After that experiment Ron sold his boat and we both stopped eating local fish. He thought it was immoral that he should sell fish if he wouldn't eat it himself. Some people might have gone on eating fish, but we know of people who had died young of cancer which we believed was because of Windscale. Bob Benson's son, who lived nearby, died young of a brain tumour and so did Alan Lockett's daughter. Both families live close to us. We had a vague feeling something was wrong. I wasn't keen on eating fish because of the sea pollution. When we did this experiment it just made our minds up that something was wrong.'

Another Barrow weekend-fisherman told me, 'I worked in the shipyard on both the nuclear powered – and armed – submarines. You know yourself that you worry, you feel a bit uneasy, but you don't let it worry you too much. My escape from it was to get out on that boat and fish in peace and quiet. I didn't know the fish I was hauling out of the water were full of that bloody stuff from Sellafield. I remember some expert explaining that that plutonium in the winkles and cockles we were eating was from the same batch that was used in the Polaris warheads being fitted into the subs. I thought that's bloody ironic that is. I've still got the boat, but my heart's not in it. I think a working man has to have something to escape to.'

For the most part our initial reaction to Greenpeace was very much from a layperson's point of view. However, there was one person in CORE at the time who really understood the issue, and that was Joe Thompson. Joe had been an industrial chemist, then a biology teacher. Joe and his wife Jean had been the tireless compaigners who had persuaded a stubborn Labour Government to hold the Windscale Inquiry in 1977.

Joe and Jean Thompson did a remarkable job in gathering together the scientists to help plead the environmentalists' case. Jean also showed great courage as she turned out to be the lone protester to 'greet' the first shipment of spent nuclear fuel from Japan as it entered Barrow.

Joe told me why he first became interested. 'I got involved in all this because I was a kid in the district and as a lad I spent a hell of a lot of time in the Duddon Estuary. In the holidays we used to spend a lot of our time on the sands and shore at Foxfield. It just appalled me that there was something, dammit, that was so polluted. They seemed to think it was their God-given right to pollute the whole Cumbrian coast. I felt I was able to do something as a kid which was going to be denied to kids now. My kids never went to the beach when they were growing up through the '70s. I've got grandchildren now and there's no way they would go in that sea. At the time of the '57 fire we didn't take daily newspapers as we lived rather out of the way. I suppose we missed the news. The local farmers didn't throw their milk away, and our kids were drinking milk directly from the local farm, directly under the cloud as it passed over the country. I suppose there's an element of bitterness in it that my kids had been taking milk contaminated with iodine, polonium, strontium and caesium and whatever else happened to be in the release. I remember saying to Donaghue, one of Sellafield's managers, that really I didn't give a damn what they did inside the factory fence so long as they kept it inside the factory fence.'

Joe, sadly, was vindicated in many of his concerns. 'The NRPB recently lowered the recommended radiation dose which they gave in evidence to the Windscale Inquiry. At no time were they willing to accept there were any dangers from low doses of radiation. Radiation hasn't suddenly become more dangerous now in 1988 than it was in 1977.

'I think the most terrible thing is that the west coast of Cumbria, in fact the west coast of England, from the south of Scotland to the north coast of Wales, has been contaminated for just the generation of a piddling little bit of energy.' Sadly, Joe died of cancer in June 1988.

The Political Ecology Research Group had been asked in 1982 to do a report on the effects of the 1987 fire at Sellafield, compared to the incidence of illness around Three Mile Island. I was one of the people involved in the basic research, collecting weather data, rainfall patterns and the like following the accident. The next step was to get the statistics from the local health authority on cancers. We were particularly interested in getting details of thyroid cancers as these are most susceptible to Iodine-131, which was released during the fire.

What happened was a complete surprise. I remember talking to a local health authority official. We asked for the relevant figures, and without even checking he said, 'They are not publicly available as they are too politically sensitive.' The resulting multiple myeloma figures which were eventually released told the full story as to why the health authority was so keen to keep things quiet. For in discussion with Japanese scientists Peter Taylor found the rate of multiple myeloma in south-west Cumbria was on the same level as the rates in Hiroshima and Nagasaki.

In September of 1983 A. P. Brown of the NRPB published a précis of a cancer report in the NRPB Bulletin. This looked at the cancer incidence for the years 1974–78 for south west Cumbria. It is estimated that the twenty excess cases of multiple myeloma amongst the 'civilian' population in south west Cumbria were equal to the excess due to radiation exposure in the nuclear workforce, worldwide, since 1920! (g 24/11/83).

In December 1984 the South Cumbria Health Authority had published their investigation into multiple myeloma rates within their region. The report, presented by Dr Stephen Horsley, started by giving several reasons for the cause of the increase in multiple myeloma. Exposure to high doses of radiation is first cited as a factor. Then comes farming, paper manufacturing, smelting and close contact with pet animals! Texts books cite radiation as the only known cause of this illness. Dr Alice Stewart, the epidemiologist who convinced the world of the link between X-raying pregnant women and increased childhood leukaemias, said, 'Radiation is the first thing you think about if you get an excess of multiple myeloma.' The report acknowledged that those who live in Barrow seemed more likely to get bone-marrow cancer than other parts of south-west Cumbria, the only part of the area bordered by the Irish Sea. However, the report concluded, 'It seems most unlikely that this (radiation) explains the excess incidence of myeloma in Barrow.' And yet the MAFF reports at the time showed that 'an ordinary member of the public who consumed fish landed at Whitehaven or Fleetwood' would get an annual dose of some 13 per cent of the annual permitted level, which was then 5 mSv. This is a dose equal to some thirteen chest X-rays!

At the time the County Medical Officer, Dr Peter Tiplady, said, 'There is a significant increase in multiple myeloma and I'm not trying to disguise that fact. I haven't got any explanation for it. It's a surprising finding because it's an isolated finding amongst the cancers that are known to be sensitive to radiation. These are quite significant and worrying increases in cancer, I won't deny that.'

One local doctor, David Todd, did find the courage to talk about the problem. He spoke out on a documentary for Channel Four's 20/20 Vision. Todd was particularly concerned with what he had seen in his own practice. 'When I was a medical student some eighteen years ago, I remember being shown a case of multiple myeloma and we were told at the time that if we were unlucky we might see one case in the whole of our professional careers. In the last eight years I've seen five cases of multiple myeloma. What's more I've seen three cases of acute myeloid or acute lymphatic leukaemias. I know that one of the causes of these illnesses can be that they are radiation induced. So my experience is that I've now had eight cases of these illnesses in eight years and I'm becoming concerned.

'They all worked in and around Barrow, some worked in the shipyard, others had nothing to do with the shipyard, but all had lived all their lives in this area.

'What concerns me is that we may be dealing with a different form of disease process than we've known up to now, in that there will be a time lag between exposure and development of the illness. My concern at this moment is that the increased incidence that we're seeing now, some twenty to twenty-five years after the fire at Windscale, shows that we are now beginning to pick up the bill in terms of health.

'I think nuclear power is the thing of the future. We can't avoid it, but if we are going to use that as our major power supply in the future we're going to have to tread more carefully.

'The people I have seen are right across the age span, including two under eleven years old. What I want to know is why this has occurred. If somebody comes along and proves to me there is another reason other than radiation I will be happy. But at the moment nobody is telling me anything and the people in this area are suffering an increased incidence of illness. I really do wish that the establishment medical officer would exhibit a bit more of an open mind about it and stop talking in terms of cluster – how big a cluster do you need for an epidemic? When we talk about radiation-induced illness we are talking about a disease entity that we do not really know the rules of. With asbestos we learned our lessons in retrospect. It took us twenty-five to thirty years to learn the lessons of asbestos which initially we thought was quite safe. Over those twenty-five to thirty years safety levels were brought down and down until we are now in a situation where they say we are to have nothing to do with asbestos. I think we are on the same time-scale of illness with radiation illness and if there are going to be lessons learned, let us learn them a little quicker.

'I am just frightened that the figures I have in my practice may be the beginnings of a rise. There is usually a twenty-five year delay between exposure and the onset of illness.'

David Todd, who is a keen fisherman, has noted the same strange markings and growths on fish that many other people have seen: 'fish which have got abnormalities on the surface, wart-like growths over the bodies. The fishermen have a name for them, "windscale fish", and throw them straight back in the water. I've seen such fish. I've caught them. I'm not a fish expert, but if these marks had happened on a human being I'd be suspecting that this person had a form of skin cancer.'

David Caldwell, former under-secretary at the DHSS in London, perhaps summed up the views of many when he said: 'I think what concerned me was the estimate which was given of a number of local people who would be likely to die as a result of the routine discharges from the new reprocessing plant. They are routine discharges and take no account of accidents and mishaps. The figure given over a ten-year period is twenty to twenty-five deaths from cancer. If by some magic we knew who those people were going to be, and we could say you, you, you and you, are going to die of cancer as a result of our work here, I think public opinion would be forced to take a different view about it. Even Lord Parker (the Inspector at the 1977 Windscale Inquiry) would have to, perhaps, take a different view about whether it was acceptable. The grief and the pain are no less because the people are not known.'

In 1984 Vickers began work on building the Trident sheds in Barrow, the huge covered docks in which the latest nuclear submarines would be built. In order to lay a foundation sand and silt were taken from the area of Walney Channel known as Roosecote sands and deposited in the Devonshire Dock. Work also began on clearing and filling in the old graving dock, right next to the sheds. Local union officials came to us as they were worried that the sand was contaminated. Vickers workers complained of dry sand getting onto the dockside they were working on and causing a problem. We had some of the mud analysed, first by Dr Richard Scott, a molecular biologist at Edinburgh University, and then by the NRPB. It was agreed the silt was contaminated and excess material dredged must never be used on agricultural land. In fact, said the NRPB, none of it should be used on flower beds outside buildings. It would be better to tarmacadam over such material to keep doses 'as low as reasonably achievable'. Men had worked on the silt all summer long.

Because of the Sellafield connection Barrow Council has applied, on several occasions, to be represented on the Sellafield local Liaison Committee, as has the South Lakes District Council. They have been refused on the grounds that they are not close enough, even though the Isle of Man has a place on the Committee.

Early in 1979 an accident had happened in the shipyard involving an empty spent fuel flask from Sellafield which had been taken into one of the engineering workshops for refurbishment. As it was turned upside down contaminated water flooded from a leaky valve that had not been replaced properly. At the time the Vickers Health and safety committee was told that there was a very low level of radioactivity in the water and there was no danger. The area of the spillage was roped off, with the infamous orange bunting (Minuted 3.5.79). As the men would sarcastically say, it's a well-known fact that radiation would not dare go past the orange bunting in Vickers. Fears of the true dangers of the spillage emerged when Vickers had the part of the floor which was contaminated jack-hammered out and dumped at Vickers' low-level tip on North Walney. A piece of the floor given to us by a Vickers worker, some three months after the accident, showed readings 10–20 times above normal for gamma radiation. In February 1980 ninety per cent of Vickers workers refused to refurbish flasks and the company lost the contract on them.

It is impossible to tell if a cancer is caused by man-made or natural radiation. Where does someone get the radiation dose that proves too much? On the beach, eating fish, at work, going home under a contaminated cloud, or is natural radiation the final straw?

What happened to the Roberts family is a case in point. They had lost their daughter Barbara when she was thirty-two. At the time of the '57 fire she was ten years old. Her parents' house was on the southern end of Walney Island. Like most children she had drunk milk at school and at home before the ban on the milk came through. Her school was at the point on Walney Island which was tested most regularly for radiation by Vickers, whose submarines were built on the opposite bank of Walney Channel, on Barrow Island. This channel is the most contaminated area of the Furness Peninsula, with levels of plutonium 1,800 times fallout having been recorded there. Not that the Roberts knew this. Like most Barrow families the Roberts loved the beaches. They were a great place to take the family for a day out. Like most other children Barbara found the beach fascinating. She used to collect winkles and cockles and continued to eat shellfish directly from the sea right the way through her five pregnancies, although only three of the children she conceived made it into the world. At twenty-two she was sterilised. In 1977 she was diagnosed as having a breast cancer. She could not bring herself to tell her parents about it until she became seriously ill. Her husband had been sworn to secrecy also. What happened between her and her doctors between 1977 and 1980 is something her parents do not know. They feel they cannot ask their son-in-law as it is too painful for him. Her mother is bitter because when she spoke to experts at Christies she was told they probably would have been able to save Barbara had she got to them early enough.

Surprisingly enough Barbara had worked until six weeks before her death. On 27 November 1981 she was found to have secondary cancers in the brain. She was told the condition was incurable and died on 19 December 1981.

Barbara had more than just a 'public' connection with nuclear power, she also had an employment connection. She worked as a cleaner on what is known as B-Block in the Vickers shipbuilding yard. This is part of the submarine dock complex and had changing rooms in it. These are the rooms where the DTOs change after they have come out of the submarines. Barbara worked in the changing rooms with other girls in a 'gang' of four on shift work. Her parents suspect that she had to deal with contaminated materials, but to her parents' knowledge Barbara did not wear any safety clothing. Three of the four girls in that cleaning squad have contracted cancer. One girl has died of a brain tumour, the third, aged twenty-nine, had a mastectomy as a result of breast cancer. It was then found out that the same girl was sterile and whilst in for her breast operation she collapsed and was found to have bone-marrow cancer. The parents don't know what happened to the fourth girl.

Mrs Roberts' sorrow is all the more acute because she nursed Barbara through the final weeks of her life when, dying from the cancer (which had spread into her brain) she would scream to be put out of her misery. 'She would lie in bed and ask me to push my hands to the side of her head to ease the pain,' Mrs Roberts told me. 'Sometimes I could hardly bear it, but I knew she didn't have long to go. I've seen too much suffering in my life. I'm originally from Aberfan. Most of my family were there when the tip moved, but at least that was that. It was terrible, but it was final. This nuclear business though, they don't know where it begins or where it ends. I remember now how daft I was in 1957. We heard the news to throw the milk away and I did that. I was just about to send Barbara to the shop for some more when I realised what I was doing. How did she come to die? Was it the accident, or was it playing on the beach, or eating the winkles?' Barbara's father vividly recalls that on cold mornings, he would stop and talk to his daughter as she leant against the spent nuclear fuel flasks for warmth, as they were being unloaded in the dock.

Other areas of the country believe they might be affected by Sellafield too. In October 1987 researchers at Lancaster University found that the coastal area of Lancaster had an increased rate of cancers. The leukaemia blackspots were Morecambe, Lytham St Annes and Fleetwood (w/n Oct. 87). The area is not only washed by the Irish Sea, but was also heavily contaminated by the 1957 fire.

To the north of the plant there is the high incidence of childhood cancers at Wampool near Maryport. In the town of Maryport itself there appears to have been a high incidence of Down's syndrome babies, similar to the high number born in Dundalk across the Irish Sea. In October 1987 the *Daily Mirror* reported that the rate of Down's syndrome babies born in Maryport was four times the national average. Most of the mothers are convinced that the 1957 fire is to blame for their child's problem. Local doctors were quick to reassure the women that there is no connection between radiation and Down's syndrome, a statement which simply cannot be proved.

The Black Report did not look in depth at this possible effect of radiation, but some reports have shown a possible link. An official UK study is now underway into the Maryport Down's syndrome children. In 1976 a study was published on Kerala in India. This has one of the world's highest natural background readings of radiation, with levels of 20 mSv being experienced in some cases, ten times higher than Britain's average rate of background radiation. Individual exposures could be greater. The report from the All India Institute of Medical Sciences in New Delhi stated that there was a higher prevalence of Down's syndrome children in the area. The illness was four times more likely to occur there than in normal radiation zones. The report stated, 'Genetic damage induced by radiation seems likely to be responsible for the high prevalence of mental retardation in the area.' (g Oct. 76). In America the Metropolitan Edison company which owned Three Mile Island denied any link between a Down's baby born in 1979, nine months after the accident, and the release of radioactivity from their plant. However, they did pay more than one million dollars' compensation to the family of the child.

There are suspicious and worried communities living near many nuclear establishments. In October 1987 the Imperial Cancer Research Fund published a report saying that children living near five nuclear plants run what is suspected to be a four-fold greater risk of dying of leukaemia. The plants were Capenhurst and Springfields (which make nuclear fuel), Aldermaston weapons research plant, Harwell, the UKAEA research station, and Amersham which makes radio-isotopes for medicine. 'Our survey shows there is an excess of childhood leukaemia, especially lymphoid leukaemia, around nuclear installations,' said Sir Richard Doll, the chief author of the report.

CHAPTER

11

It is well known, that among the blind the one-eyed man is king.
'Adagia', Gerard Erasmus.

In the early days there was considerable ignorance as to the real purpose of Sellafield, but some local people quickly latched on. In 1949 a Mr Jackson wrote, 'The sense of helplessness in the face of arbitrary decisions of government authorities is a defect in democracy. Surely the worst feature of the atomic energy plants is not the danger to their surroundings, but the diabolical purpose behind their construction. We hear something of medical and agricultural uses for radioactive elements and a little about industrial power in many years' time, but everyone suspects that the high priority in the employment of scientists and fleets of vehicles at taxpayers' expense is accorded on account of the military potentialities of atomic energy. The phrase "defence needs" is sometimes used to describe this. In fact it means the power and the intention, whenever a military conflict arises, to inflict a repetition of the Hiroshima destruction with its death toll of 70,000 civilians with agonising slow deaths for a large proportion, instead of useful peace-time production, that the industry and resources.' (w/n 20.10.49). The sense of priorities has not changed in forty years.

But not everyone saw it like that, and even after the 1957 fire an editorial in the *Whitehaven News* still managed to express confidence in the plant. 'Windscale has given work to thousands of West Cumbrians for the past ten years. It was largely due to Windscale's need of scientists and technicians that the Whitehaven College of Further Education was built. The coming of Windscale opened up a new future for hundreds of young people in West Cumberland. To man Windscale and train our own youth hundreds of highly skilled, highly educated people have been drafted into the area, hundreds of houses have been built at Egremont and Whitehaven to house them and a new school built at Seascale for their children. The life of the district has been enriched in every way through the developments at Windscale and an even more prosperous future is assured by further developments now in progress. We are proud of Windscale and Calder Hall and we in West Cumberland have little fear for the future.

'Recently we have had to pay for our place in this new industry just as we have had to pay the price of being a coal and iron ore mining area. Let us not forget that the latter industries have cost hundreds of lives and the new one has focused the eyes of the world on this little corner of Britain. Then we will keep the events of the past few weeks in perspective.'

The invading army, with its prodigy, had taken control. The resentment of the new schools, houses and colleges afforded the off-comers had been suppressed by the all-too-desperate need to work. The locals had failed to notice how they were being exploited.

Some 'off-comers' did make the effort to fit into and settle down with the community, such as Les Tuley. 'I came here in 1958. In those days the UKAEA was very prestigious, and for a chemist, like myself, it was a job you wanted to get into. Before that I had worked in the oil industry. Until 1978 I worked as a chemist in the research and development labs at Sellafield. I moved over to the public relations side after the Whitehaven Inquiry.'

Les gives a very different view of how some people feel about living close to Sellafield. 'I live just outside the fence at Seascale. I've brought up my own family there, four children, fingers crossed, they are now married and having children themselves. There's never been anything wrong with them. They've swum in the sea as much as anybody. In terms of the quality of life, most of the local people I think have a very good quality. I know you can argue about that. There may not be West End theatres and things of that nature, but on the other hand there are the hills, the lakes, the sea-shore and my family have all been very happy here.

'I felt the work very interesting and very satisfying so I've been happy. Being a scientist I was fully aware of what was being discharged into the Irish Sea and into the atmosphere. I had to think about that, but when I look at what is discharged from other industries, I was quite convinced that the nuclear industry was the cleanest of industries. In those early days, techniques were not as advanced as they are today. The safety standards are far higher now than they were. Yet in those days compared with what I'd been working in they were far better here. I felt safety was a priority here. In the oil industry, I used to wash the benches in benzine with my bare hands. Benzine is now regarded as one of the most carcinogenic substances there is.'

Les is ever anxious to point out the financial implications of Sellafield to Copeland: 'In terms of economics the wages and salary bill from the factory, if you take into account the contractors, is well over £100 million per year. That kind of money going into the local economy certainly helps to promote business. The whole economy of the locality obviously is sustained by Sellafield. I don't feel that is a healthy thing, that it does depend on one industry, and therefore I am very pleased that the company is taking initiatives in conjunction with the county council and the local district council to see if they can promote other industries which may well at first depend on Sellafield and its new projects, but one would hope that they would establish a wider base and be able to exist in their own right and develop their trade elsewhere. I am convinced the management want to be part of the community and have certainly done their best. I know there are times when not everybody would agree and I know there are times when they are possibly accused of being heavy handed, not telling everybody everything. There may have been times when there have been misunderstandings and misquotations and that, but in general my feeling now as part of the management, is that we want to be part of the community. Working in the exhibition centre is all part of the operation of telling people what we do here, and why we do it.

'There is a feeling now that the longer-term problems are jobs and employment. We'll see, from now, the thrust of their efforts will be to try and create jobs. There is going to be a problem when the new projects start to come to completion. When you look at the composition of the construction workforce, in many cases it's 50, 60 and even 70 per cent local labour, there is going to be an impact.

'The company is looking to that period when we've really got to try to provide and create some more jobs. There will be people there who will be losing their jobs within four or five years' time. It is certainly something that worries the local politicians because it is not an easy area of the country to attract employment to. If we can use the momentum that has been created by the new projects to set up industries which can establish themselves then we would hope that the area would be in a better position.'

Les Tuley works in the exhibition centre which cost £5 million to build. BNFL have admitted that their PR budget is £8.1 million a year. The company's concern for alternative work has to be measured against the £1 million a year, for ten years, they are putting into the jobs initiative scheme. In 1984 BNFL gave Copeland Council £600,000 for a running track at Whitehaven. In the same year the County Council gave the same amount to the BNFL for apprentice training, thus leading people to comment that rate-payers were funding BNFL's PR.

West Cumbria looks as if it might well get dragged further into the nuclear mire. Almost every plan for new jobs has been linked to Sellafield in some way. Two of the proposals are for a nuclear dump or a new reactor on site. The third is to have a science park next to Sellafield to promote British technology. As an idea in itself it is good, but once again it leans too heavily on the nuclear industry.

Les Tuley has seen the ups and downs of the nuclear industry. He started at the plant just after the Suez crisis, when dearer oil was a good incentive for an alternative energy. Les believes the magnox programme has proved to be successful. He recalls, 'In the '60s, when nuclear power went into the doldrums, I can remember looking up my redundancy number because we all thought that was it. Oil was cheap again and so was coal. It was only when the Middle East troubles flared again in the mid-70s and the price of oil quadrupled in about six months or even less, suddenly nuclear power was back in vogue again. There had been a lack of investment in the nuclear industry, particularly in reprocessing, which I think we paid for later on. It was only in the '70s when the new investment programme started to roll again. By that time there were new types of reactors coming along and from that point on the future looked rosy again.'

The future does not look quite so good at present. 'The nuclear industry is looking with some trepidation towards electricity privatisation. If nuclear power has to compete with coal from British coal fields, that's one thing. If it has to compete with cheap

189

imported coal then the nuclear industry may be put at some disadvantage. I would hope that the nuclear industry is not put into a situation where it is virtually left isolated, can't expand or would find it difficult to expand.'

The present BNFL chairman Christopher Harding was taken on in 1986 to get the company ready for privatisation within three years long before privatisation of nuclear power itself was mentioned. In direct contradiction of earlier statements Harding is now anxious to point out that it will not be privatised, a sure indicator of the money market's faith in their performance. In September 1989 the Public Accounts Committee of the Commons published a highly critical report on the company's financial acumen. It noted that the company's rate of return was lower 'than those of all large industrial and commercial companies in the UK' and that there should be an independent review of the company's ever-increasing costs.

When I interviewed Les Tuley the debate over the future of reprocessing in Germany was at its height. 'The French in Cap de Hague are the only real competitors. The Japanese are building theirs. The Germans are beginning to build theirs at Wackersdorf. People like the French for example, 70 per cent of their electricity is produced by nuclear power. They are looking to sell that, if they can get the European market they would be quite happy to sell that. I view with two minds the expansion of the reprocessing from abroad. In one sense it is the nuclear industry expanding, in another sense it's competition. Presumably nationalistic attitudes would mean that certainly if Germany builds one they would do the German reprocessing which would mean less business for us.'

Les told me, 'I have met quite a number of people from Wackersdorf, both elected politicians and people that live round there. After we talked to them I think they went away more knowledgeable and I hope some of their fears were allayed. I think they are subjected to a fair barrage, just as we are in this country, of media writings about the nuclear industry. Not always factual and not always objective. My advice to them is to accept it and make it work for them, in other words that the community around about can benefit, both in jobs and economics, quality of life, everything.'

As it turns out, the Germans' quality of life will not be affected. In place of a reprocessing plant they are to have a car recycling plant and a solar cell factory. Soon after I spoke to Les it was announced that they had decided to give up on the idea of reprocessing as it is considered uneconomic. They are now considering sending 4,000 tonnes of oxide fuel to Sellafield.

Tony Hildrop is a local councillor who also worked for BNFL and who believes fervently in the industry. 'I know of no other industry anywhere in the world that has had the social responsibility for an area that BNFL has had. That may sound a bit over the top. People say they are buying the local community to keep quiet. I don't believe it is bribery. It has given Copeland financial stability which it lacked in the 1930's. As a youngster I used to come walking over here and the area was dreary and depressed. The arrival of the UKAEA made a big difference. I have great reservations about being a one-industry area. In recent years the industry has tried to give contracts locally to support businesses. For instance the transport "coffins" were made at Workington steel works until it closed.'

The type of 'buying' that Hildrop refers to comes not just in the form of rates, which everybody has to pay, but in the numerous donations and sponsorship deals that BNFL indulge in. For example they gave £100,000 to Whitehaven Rugby League, with an extra £60,000 for a new player. Then there was the £1,500 money spent on sponsoring a horse race in Carlisle, hardly an essential to the Cumbrian infrastructure.

But despite BNFL's generosity many people are now beginning to tire of endless nuclear expansion. Hildrop has certain reservations about the idea of a nuclear dump in the area. 'The principal argument is locally that while we generally accept the nuclear industry we are not happy if the repository is used as an international dump. We have been assured by NIREX and BNFL that the contracts they have for the Thermal Oxide Reprocessing Plant and all the rest contain clauses that any waste arising will be sent back to the country of origin along with any recycled fuel that they are entitled to. If that is kept up then maybe I'm not too unhappy with that.' In fact on 21st March 1989 BNFL admitted that one-quarter of the nuclear waste from foreign contracts would remain in Britain as they had not negotiated to return it.

At least Tony Hildrop will never stand accused of being anything but consistent in his beliefs. The man who once read a science fiction book on nuclear power still has as much faith in the industry, even after thirty years. 'I support nuclear energy very strongly. The benefits of nuclear energy have not yet been reached. I can't see them being reached in our lifetime, so much good can come out of it it, so much good can be made from it. I've seen demonstrations of some of the tidal wave stations, the bobbing ducks, and the like. The idea of wind farms doesn't appeal to me. I'd hate to see great wind farms stuck on some of the hillsides around. They would be a much greater visual distraction than any nuclear power station. I believe we can't afford to go on burning coal, not only because of the acid rain problem, but because it's too valuable a mineral to be burnt at only 40 per cent efficiency.'

What concerns Tony Hildrop most is what he sees as distortion by the media. 'We are faced with exaggeration in press reports. I've done interviews with people and because it's not what they wanted to hear the interviews have not been shown. I've seen interviews I've done quoted completely out of context, misrepresented. I try as hard as possible to be fair. I could go on for hours about the crazy stories produced by the press on the nuclear industry. I don't know of any other industry which has a triple back up. For example, if your control system on a nuclear reactor goes wrong (which controls the chain reaction and stops explosions) you have a back-up system, only in the nuclear industry you have a three-stage system so that if any two of those three fail then this one will be there to control it. I'm sure the people of Flixborough would have been happy if they had a triple back-up system. Things like that are never said.'

Hildrop did add that he supported Greenpeace in what they did except when it came to Sellafield. His stance is a theme common to many statements I have heard from people within the industry. If Greenpeace goes to Billingham to protest there against chemical dumping the workers at that site say they support Greenpeace on everything except the chemical industry. Such people are no different from all the Conservative voters in the south of England who fought so hard to stop low-level nuclear dumps in their areas.

Tony Hildrop, given a BEM in the 1984 honours list, is best known in his role as Chairman of the Cumbria Tourist Board. He finished work when he had a heart attack, something he puts down to overwork due to trade unions and politics. Although he took early retirement he is still very active. The Tourist Board takes up a lot of his time. He is proud of the fact that when he first took the post the Cumbrian Tourist Board only had 600 members, it now has 1400, one of the highest in the country. He is keen to see the tourist net spread wider than the 'honey pot' of the Lake District and believes BNFL goes a long way to encouraging visitors to West Cumbria. West coast hoteliers also benefit from BNFL's workforce.

'The idea of a nuclear dump hasn't affected the tourist business. There are a lot of doubts being cast upon that particular idea from the local population. The vast majority of the establishments in the Sellafield area are happy, because the beds are filled Monday to Friday with contractors and so on. If you were to take a weekly bed count you might find some of the west coast hotels do better than some Lake District places. The west coast people have the business the full twelve months of the year. The position has been changing over the years, there are more tourists coming into this area now and Sellafield is responsible for a large number of them. Last year they had 150,000 through the exhibition centre. Local people are trying to tie in so that people don't just visit the exhibition centre, but go to other places as well, such as the Eskdale railway, or Muncaster Castle. There's a much greater acceptance of BNFL throughout the county from a tourist point of view.'

However, a number of local tourist spots have had a falling off in interest because of Sellafield. Nor have all the link-ups succeeded. Sellafield used to advertise a bus trip between Little Ratty steam railway and the Calder Reactors, called the 'Two Ages of Steam'. It was abandoned due to lack of interest.

One town that felt it had something to offer by way of marine attraction was Maryport. The harbour is one of the most attractive in the county, and the sandstone buildings of the town are far prettier than the red brick uniformity of a place like Barrow. All throughout 1983 dredging had been going on in the harbour to make room for the yachts and boats which would, it was hoped, be attracted to a marina and maritime museum which were being planned. Then the worst happened. The silt from the harbour was to be used on a children's playground. Concerned locals feared that it would be contaminated. Dr Richard Scott, who had tested the Barrow silt, analysed the Maryport samples and expressed the view that it was too radioactive to be used. The county council called in the National Radiological Protection Board, expecting that Scott's claims would prove to be unfounded. In something of a shock report (kept confidential but then leaked), the NRPB agreed with Scott. They believed that in order to keep radiation doses 'as low as reasonably achievable' that it would be better not to use the silt. But in a measure which showed the real concern over this silt the council had it dumped back in the Solway Firth. This caused an uproar locally. If the silt was unsafe when brought onto land then surely it was unsafe lying on the beaches. Professor Fremlin told the county council the mud was safe. Obviously no one believed him. An ironic twist to the tale is that in order to dump the silt back at sea the Council had to obtain a special licence from the Department of Environment as nuclear dumping had, by this time, been outlawed by the London Dumping Convention.

In 1985 BNFL gave £350,000 to the Maryport harbour project. The money was part of the West Cumbrian infrastructure payments (although Maryport lies outside the area which is supposed to receive such payments).

It is unusual for people who are critical of the nuclear industry to get elected in Copeland. One exception is Marjorie Higham, the councillor for the area which includes the Drigg dump. When she stood as a Councillor for Drigg she got the biggest majority in the district. As an ex-Sellafield worker, whose husband still works at the plant, she feels that lapses in safety standards have let down what could have been a good industry.

'I used to be on the Local Liaison Committee because I was the Councillor for Drigg. It was only because I was on that committee that I became aware of what was happening. At the first meeting I knew most of the people, I had worked with a number of them, at Sellafield. I sort of thought this is all very nice. At the second meeting I went to, there was mention of someone who lived at Maryport who had been on Border TV programme saying the fish out of the sea had got diseases and it was due to the discharges. They were discussing this in all seriousness. I thought it was hilarious, here's this great company bothered about what somebody was saying about the fish being diseased. As far as I was aware only some innocuous stuff went into the sea. The man they were discussing had a telephone number which belonged to the County Council, for whom he worked. I thought, there's something wrong here. I couldn't talk to anybody about what went on at this meeting because it was all secret, including the minutes. This was 1974 and I think BNFL were wanting the discharge levels increased again. That's what was bothering them. They had got to eighty per cent of the then limit and they were in a quandary about what to do and they were going to shut the plant down, if they didn't have these levels increased. Instead they had to start to do something to cut the discharges down. I began to look at the sea discharges and I realised to my horror that they were putting plutonium in the sea. I was shocked.

'Then in 1976 the Flowers Report was published and that mentioned Drigg. I had been led to believe that only trace active stuff was dumped, like a rubbish tip. I didn't realise until 1976 that they were storing plutonium contaminated waste in those magazines. I'd never been told, despite the fact I was on the committee. As the UKAEA they hadn't needed planning permission for anything they did as they were a Government department. Once they made this pseudo-company, BNFL, they then had to be under the planning laws, a little inconvenient. In 1971 they had to relicense Drigg storage depot as it was under a private company. I was saying it's quite all right, they always stick to the book. I was quoting all the safety levels, and it's only for low level waste. The NII people drew my attention to the report and wanted me to fuss about it at the inquiry. It wasn't until the Windscale 1977 Inquiry that it became public knowledge. It wasn't till then that I really took much interest in anything that happened because in all that time I assumed that these people wouldn't have done anything that would have put anybody at risk. In my innocence I assumed everybody stuck to the rules.'

Marjorie finally won her battle to have that plutonium contaminated waste moved. It is to be sent to Sellafield for better storage.

But her fight has caused her many heartaches and many problems. 'The majority of people living around here work at the plant and you can tell they don't want to know you in case their jobs are at risk if they are seen talking to a dissident. The reason I was so incensed about it is I spent six years as a training officer teaching people how to handle radioactive materials so it was safe for them and safe for everybody else. I was under the mistaken impression that everybody in the works worked to the book and that they all knew about the dangers and they worked so that neither they nor their colleagues were going to be exposed to any radiation. If it's handled properly it's perfectly safe, if you use the right amount of distance and shielding. I assumed this stuff I was putting down the drain was recycled through the plant and it never occurred in my wildest dreams that that stuff was going straight in the sea. After the 1983 accident I began to realise that that effluent plant was still in the same state as when it was built in the '40's and in the '80's. Forty years later the same plant was being used. It had been modified occasionally, but of course they show people how to do things and after forty years they'd been doing it totally wrong. I knew how it should have worked. I feel let down by the whole thing and my other ex-colleagues felt the same when they found out. I was talking to this gentleman in Seascale and he put it this way: "We thought," he said to me, "that all these people were honourable people doing the right thing." I believe that if they take the care and spend the money on it, it will be tolerable, but they cannot afford another accident of any shape or sort.'

Even the clergy of Cumbria are caught up in the mass of contradictions about the plant. In private discussions I have had with local church men the feeling has been that in order to cater for their flocks they need to defer to their worldly needs. That means let them work for a decent wage, don't criticise them and hopefully everything will be all right. A local priest told me that he felt himself to be as hypocritical as the rest. His church collections were made up almost entirely of money from BNFL wages packets, yet the company made plutonium for weapons of mass destruction and polluted the environment. What was he to do? If he scolded them they would simply turn away from him and then their spiritual lives would be empty. In short this priest faced the same dilemma as many in Cumbria who depend on the nuclear industry.

12

Cowardice asks the question, Is it safe?
Expedience asks the question, Is it politic?
Vanity asks the question, Is it popular?
But conscience asks the question, Is it right?
Martin Luther King Jnr

A psychological report was once compiled on the workers at Sellafield. It was completed in 1982 and was never publicised until CORE leaked it in 1986. The report had been compiled at the company's behest. It was not kind to the management. It stated, 'If workers' human needs and characteristics are ignored or neglected it is likely that some will neglect aspects of their duty which are essential to safety and security. There is an obsolete attitude which makes it difficult for the company to understand or react appropriately to public pressures and complaints about leaks, secrecy and so on and staff's complaints about the system.'

Wilkinson compared the rich BNFL with a much smaller firm and its commitment to staff care. 'What is ironic is that Rowntree Mackintosh, which is a toffee-making company, employs several psychologists on its staff, whereas BNFL, who have thousands of employees involved in the potentially deadly process of turning radioactive waste into plutonium, have no properly qualified psychologist at all working in their Windscale plant. It is no way to run a modern industry, to take the attitude that "Staff should be stretched and if we have to cause a few nervous breakdowns on the way that's just too bad." (comment from a Windscale department head). From the company's point of view, if it has insufficient knowledge of its employees as individuals, how will it know how many of them are accident-prone, incompetent or dangerous, experiencing personal problems which affect their capacity for efficient work or make them vulnerable in other ways?

'I would suggest there is a need for expert advice on assessment and selection of personnel, not just for the above reasons, or because this is common practice in many large companies nowadays, but also because I have been surprised at times, when I have had contact with some Windscale staff referred to Psychiatry and Psychology, that such obviously disturbed people were employed at the plant in the first place (sometimes in "sensitive" posts). Some similar points could be made about the personality and suitability of some of the scientific staff. Many of these staff appear to be constitutionally "neurotic" and unstable. One of my psychiatric colleagues has asked the question whether e.g. Windscale "actually sets out to employ anxious obsessionals, or whether they just make them that way in the end".'

Wilkinson was not trying to write himself into a job. The report makes it quite obvious he did not want the extra work. 'Professional counselling facilities should exist in a large industrial organisation, for occasions when people's personal lives go wrong. There are examples of Windscale staff who are "under stress" on my case load and I do sometimes feel that it would help the company if there were an independent advisor.

'Windscale workers pass through the pyschiatric casualty systems at the local general hospital at a considerable rate, and it would be necessary to multiply the yearly numbers of those who are formally referred by a factor of five, or ten, or get a closer estimate of the proportions of the workforce with psychiatric or psychological problems. That means a lot of people, with a lot of problems, daily travelling in and out of a plutonium factory.

'There is little I can say about the management structure except that it seems to breed tension. I know there has recently been a shake-up and the system has been revamped to incorporate so called "modern management techniques". Basically the management structures now seem to be multi-layered hierarchies of the most traditional kind and it is hard to see what is modern about that. Various "princes" head up departments which are seen as their individual empires, which they certainly defend as if they were. There then begins the back-biting and paranoia which is common at middle management levels in bureaucratic organisations. A senior scientist described the system to me as "totalitarian". Apart from safety there are security issues, which would complicate anyone's attempt to create a liberal democratic management style in the factory.'

These are not the words of a man who has encountered a happy and relaxed workforce. After the release of the report BNFL admitted that they still have no psychologists on site. But they did say that 'twenty-five per cent of all people going to a doctor will have a psychological base to their illness. Even then the main factor of their stress is likely to be domestic – marital problems, financial trouble or the health of one of the family. With a work-force of 11,000 people you are bound to encounter all sorts of problems – as will any industry. This company is confident that it has a well-trained, motivated and responsible workforce at every level – management through to shop floor.' (w/n Feb. 1986).

Kay Appleton saw quite a different reason for the problems at the plant. 'I hate to say this, but there are two workforces there. There is an educated workforce and a poorly educated one, through no fault of their own. They didn't understand it and didn't care about the discharges. Most of them didn't care while I worked there. A lot of the people on the science side cared, but because it was their job, were too loyal to do anything about it. That work-force was drawn from about the 1960s. Nowadays people move into a job, and if they think it's not good enough they will move out again in a few years. Sellafield was very lucky, they got a lot of scientists in the 1960's who had this loyalty to the Government. You don't have it now, but you did then. They have been able to rely on that section of management, which after all, runs the whole show, and was very, very loyal. They weren't prepared ever to blow the whistle on anybody in Sellafield.'

Tony Hildrop, who was a shop steward at the plant, is one of those loyal workers. But he would refute any allegation of blind allegiance. He is also honest enough to admit that working in the industry made him blind to some of its faults. 'Since I've retired from BNFL now, I try to work out some of the things perhaps I didn't see when I was involved much more closely, but I can take a much more relaxed view of things. You become entrenched, you become an automatic defender. I suppose it's natural instinct, you're looking after your own job. I still strongly believe in the future of nuclear energy because in spite of all the waste problems

I do believe it's the only clear way forward for generation of electrical energy.' He believes that the industry has had an unjustifiably bad press and that plays on the public's fear. He once told me that people got too emotionally involved in the nuclear debate to look at it properly, but aren't men like him, who saw their boyhood dreams fulfilled, emotionally involved too? Are the reactors they worked so hard to build not regarded as something more than machines to produce electricity?

Tom Touhy, for example, is very proud not only of his role in fighting the fire, but also of the role he had with the first team of people in the history of the nuclear industry. 'Calder Hall was built in three years and came in at the quoted price. What's happening with great big beautiful British industry now? I don't know if Dungeness B is operating yet. I think it's ten or twelve years late and at about four times the costs. The UKAEA had been so brilliantly successful. We went from zero to the world's first nuclear power station in ten years. That is fantastic. Never been done before. Never been done again.' And because of this Tom is annoyed at what he sees as attempts to hide the past. 'I refuse to call the place Sellafield. The place is Windscale and Calder, names to be proud of, not to be ashamed of. Things that were done down there in the early days were absolutely wonderful. I enjoyed my working life, it was tremendous. It was really exciting.'

However, even though Tom held Britain's first cache of plutonium he is now set against nuclear weapons. 'We were kidding ourselves we were a great power. I felt the same way and nearly everybody in the project felt the same way. America had this weapon and for security reasons we felt we should have it before somebody else got it. As far as I'm concerned you can take them all away. I will have nothing to do with them in this country. If anybody is lunatic enough to start using these things then if you have any on your territory you are going to be wiped out. For our little island it would be curtains.

The early research scientists revelled in the grandiose names coined for the newly found substances. One famous article by Schofield and Dolphin starts off explaining how plutonium had been called after Pluto, the God of the Underworld. The implication was clear – these men had not only found a new energy source and powerful military weapon, they had also tamed a sinister deity. They were the new alchemists toying with the very matter of the universe. But back on planet earth they were faced with more mundane problems, such as how to get rid of the effluent streams from the reprocessing plant at Windscale. The 'scientific' answer was to dump their problem into the sea. Not that the discharges were kept 'as low as reasonably achievable', quite the opposite. Answering questions about Sellafield's marine discharges in 1958 Dr John Dunster said, 'The intention has been to discharge fairly substantial amounts of radioactivity as part of an organised and deliberate scientific experiment and the aims of this experiment would have in fact been defeated if the level of activity discharged had been kept to a minimum.' (Environmental Aspects of the Large-scale Use of Atomic Energy, Geneva, September 1958).

People like the union leader Bill Maxwell probably did not realise what was going on until well after the decisions were made. His determination to stand by the industry when it all became public was probably the result of the balancing act many working men take in the search for secure employment. Bill took early retirement from Sellafield in 1988 because of ill health. He certainly had a splendid send-off from his workmates, trade union colleagues and the management. At his retirement party he echoed the well recognised family theme: 'Community unity is the most important thing. Over the years my pride and joy has been the loyalty given me. Life is all about people helping each other. Unity in the community has been what made me tick.' (e/n 2.9.88). Early this year I learnt that Bill Maxwell had cancer. Although I have been known to curse Bill in the past, through writing this book I have come to have a renewed respect for him. If he is guilty of any crime then it has been his closed door policy to outsiders. He is the typical West Cumbrian who lives and breathes for his patch. Bill never really looked beyond his own backyard. Many who met him tell of how defensive he was, how he alone would often be the only union person you were allowed to speak to. It is not just journalists who have told me this, but well-connected union and industry people as well. But whatever his faults Bill did what he probably thought was best for his people and there's not many you can say that about.

What of the other Cumbrians though, who have to do the best

for their people? Dr Barrie Walker, the Seascale GP, although an outsider to day-to-day machinations of the plant, is privy to the concerns of those who work there. Barrie voiced a common West Cumbrian worry, 'I think the most terrifying part of BNFL is that they're all powerful, they think they're all powerful. They almost think now they own West Cumbria. The management structure is such that they've got a policy, the party line. They dare not rock the boat or question.

There is a cytology unit at Sellafield which deals with all the testing for possible genetic effects in samples sent from local hospitals. New additions to the unit have led BNFL to claim it is the best such unit in the north of England. That such sensitive testing should be done by BNFL, when the health service is short of cash, is something which worries many local people. But Barrie Walker does not see it that way. 'I trust the medical scientists on site, such as the ones who run the cytology unit. But I can see the point about it being inside the fence and no access to data, although I trust them in the work they are doing.'

Of course the industry will tell you there is nothing to worry about. They are not some sinister organisation but an open and honest bunch. BNFL would deny that there is any secrecy, in fact they would tell you that they are more open now than ever.

The first travelling exhibition on nuclear power toured Cumbria in 1947! That exhibition was 'to teach the family about atomic energy'. The public would be made 'atomic energy conscious'. One can imagine the Pathe-news style presentations. Lectures, film shows, public meetings and 'brains trusts' were organised during the week of the grand tour. Scientists measured radio-activity with Geiger counters, the splitting of the atom, the eighth wonder of the modern world! In short an exhibition pretty much like the one visitors are now invited to at Sellafield. In 1961 the innocent enthusiasm was still there, there were great plans for nuclear power. Cumbrian papers ran a story that new Cunard liners would be nuclear-powered. The prototype advanced gas cooled reactor was regarded as the most likely form of ship propulsion! (w/n 18.4.84). In 1963 the plant held its first open day.

The public relations machine has taken a more front-stage role of late with BNFL going on a veritable spending spree with tax payers' money. BNFL have donated £7,000 to Barrow's rugby team and £4,000 for Walney bird reserve. They sponsored a national Sea Angling league competition in 1983. They give money to the Workington Reds (football team) and are the main sponsors for the Lowther Horse trials, which the Duke of Edinburgh frequents. One year they gave money to Carlisle United's match with Birmingham City. In September 1988 BNFL stepped in and saved a brass band concert with a £3,000 sponsorship deal (w/n 29.9.88). In 1986 BNFL sponsored an excavation of a Roman wall in Carlisle at a cost of £50,000 per year for five years (w/n 18.9.86). They even advertise on the car and bus tickets in Copeland. One legend reads 'BNFL Sellafield provides local jobs'. In 1987, the year after Chernobyl, the Government subsidy to the National Radiological Protection Board was half of that paid to Covent Garden Opera. Oddly enough the name Copeland means 'bought land'.

Les Tuley, head of BNFL public relations, denies that the company is currying favour. 'It is always a difficult field where you get industry helping the local community because like everybody else they want to be loved. There is always a danger that if you give one particular organisation some money then you make another one jealous so you've got to try to be fair and be seen to be fair and it's not always easy that. BNFL always tries to help all organisations, particularly charitable organisations and leisure, the running track and other projects like restoring some of the old property in the middle of Whitehaven. That was much appreciated by people.'

Like many within the industry, Les is not happy with the ever-present image of nuclear weapons. 'I have always been conscious that many people are concerned about nuclear weapons. I think nuclear weapons are an awful thing, but so are chemical and conventional weapons. Whether you're blown to bits by an ordinary shell or a nuclear one it's certainly not much help to those who are killed by it.'

Sellafield's role in nuclear weaponry might be less controversial were the company to allow full access to the reprocessing line by the international Euratom inspection team. That organisation oversees the treaty which controls the spread of nuclear weapons technology and material. Because BNFL reprocesses military plutonium alongside the 'civilian' counterpart Euratom are denied proper access. An ongoing battle in the European Parliament has still to resolve the issue.

Tuley knows that the weapons connection is not the only public relations challenge facing BNFL. 'I accept that people associate cancer with radiation. They don't necessarily associate it quite as closely with chemicals and drugs and things like that, but being a chemist I do know that many things are carcinogenic not just radiation and therefore there should be controls on all these things.'

Les believes there are a lot of benefits. He knows his job depends on making people see those benefits and feeling at ease with Sellafield. The public relations department of BNFL took off during the mid-70s. 'I have the impression just before Chernobyl that the public were quite happy with nuclear power stations. Then Chernobyl happened and I think that moved the goal posts. People who had been happy with nuclear power suddenly had doubts about nuclear power stations. By that time Sellafield was beginning to show that it was putting its house in order if it had ever been out of order.'

Tuley is pleased with the success of the new exhibition centre, which has attracted many more people to Sellafield over the past two years. 'New plants coming on in the past two or three years and the public coming in in greater numbers I think has made them far happier with Sellafield. Chernobyl certainly, it made life difficult for the nuclear industry because people could see that a major accident was possible. Up to that point, there was only the 1957 fire, which was kind of in the dim and distant past almost.'

I have no doubt that Les Tuley holds his views sincerely. 'I think that nuclear power is the cleanest and when I read what comes out of a coal-powered station it horrifies me. Apart from the number of people killed in coal mines and other things, the poisons, the lead discharged, not in a few ounces, or pounds, but in tons, and the radioactivity released. When you think of the valuable materials that they burn, just in order to boil water. To me that's criminal. I cannot really understand why the environmentalists don't direct their efforts at that because it's such a massive pollution. Those kinds of problems are far greater than anything that the nuclear industry causes, although I do agree with all the controls that are put on. I think that controls should be going onto the coal-fired plants particularly when you look at the tonnes of toxic gases, like sulphur dioxide.'

But although the industry is keen to point out the hazards of other industries, like coal-mining, it rarely, if ever, shows the front-end environmental impact of nuclear power. This book has dealt with the back-end waste products at places like Sellafield, but what of where the uranium is mined? A recent contract that the CEGB were chasing to mine three and a half million tonnes of uranium in Northern Canada will leave behind fifty million tonnes of radioactive waste. That same mine will also irrevocably damage the local terrain and the lifestyle of the native Indian population.

BNFL, as a partner in the Dutch, German and English consortium URENCO, has found itself in trouble over the buying of Namibian uranium. Trading in uranium from Namibia is internationally outlawed by UN treaty as the country is illegally occupied by South African forces. Until 1984 seventy-five per cent of all the uranium coming into Britain was from Namibia.

Peter Levitt, the Seascale Methodist Minister, shares many of Les Tuley's views. 'I feel there is the problem of perception and of images of nuclear power. The mushroom cloud is an image which is always going to be with us and it stirs irrational feelings and they are not always easily handled. I think it was a very good move on the part of BNFL to open up the site as much as they were able to have visitors. There's no point in trying to just do it by talking heads on TV. Meeting people at the plant made a big difference. I have been on the site a few times, a small Christian fellowship meets on site every week.

'I think there is a high degree of responsibility recognised by those working there. I know some of those who are at reasonably high level who I have been able to talk to and I don't see that there's any sort of cavalier attitude there at all. They are well aware of danger and the complexities of using radioactive materials. I've never felt that they've treated the workforce or the local community in a way which was irresponsible.'

When the Duke of Edinburgh opened the new exhibition centre he was probably introduced to the manager Paul Wilson. Wilson once told a meeting I was at that although he came from Egremont, two miles from Sellafield, he knew of no-one with cancer. I later learnt that Wilson's father-in-law, one of the

Sellafield plant managers, was found to be suffering from myeloid leukaemia at the time and was suing BNFL for compensation! Both men, who were very pro-nuclear, have since left the company.

In December 1986, when the Irish Government called for the closure of Sellafield a BNFL spokesman, in a mood of *détente*, said, 'The decision by the Irish Parliament is completely irrational and bears no relation to the facts.' (w/n Dec. 1986).

Despite the best efforts of BNFL's PR machine, Dorothy Bateman summed it up: 'I don't blame the ordinary workers in this, they are cogs just like us. They don't have any choice. It's the ones who run the place, who dictate behind the scenes. I don't know what the people who run Sellafield think. Do they go to bed at night and sleep soundly? How do they live with their consciences? What goes on in their minds? What is their morality, what do they want from life, what do they want for the future?'

Whatever the men who oversee Sellafield want is not instantly obvious, but sometimes what the local populace wants is. In August 1984 Seascale asked BNFL for money to help it build a swimming pool. Farmer Ken Mawson, a Seascale parish councillor, said, 'I can't see many people wanting to go swimming in the sea now. I haven't been swimming in the sea off the local beaches for nearly ten years because of the sewage and radioactive waste discharges. There's a lot of people who think the same way. Other areas have been successful in getting help with recreational facilities from BNFL, but up until now Seascale hasn't had a penny.' BNFL were not keen on the idea, saying that they had already given £84,000 to Copeland Council for amenities within its boundary (w/n Aug. 1984). Come January 1986 the residents of Seascale were still trying to finalise their sports facilities. In two years they had raised £7,000 and had received £11,000 from other bodies. BNFL had donated only £3,000. Another £20,000 was needed to finish all the indoor and outdoor arrangements. It was not lost on the Seascale people that BNFL had spent £20,000 moving six pigeon lofts out of the way for the running track that was being built.

What of future developments in the industry? Although the policy of MP Jack Cunningham's sponsoring union, the General Municipal and Boilermakers, is to oppose the building of pressurised water reactors, in early 1989 Cunningham was backing the idea of a pressurised water reactor at Sellafield. He welcomed the jobs it would bring. By mid-May he was saying that conservation is the best way of allaying the greenhouse effect. By mid-June BNFL announced that they might build a coal or gas powered plant on site instead of a nuclear one in order to maintain a secure supply of electricity. Cunningham's views on the latest scheme were not made known. What is known though is that Cunningham has had a lot to say over the Labour Party policy on nuclear power. The present environmental campaign is very much geared to getting the Labour Party to promise to abandon Sizewell B if they take power. However, at the annual meeting of the Nuclear Free Zones in 1989, the party's environment spokesperson, MP Joan Walley, said that Labour would decide on such issues if and when it took control. In November 1989 the Conservative government decided to abandon all PWR building except Sizewell B.

Of course the unions on site, including the General Municipal and Boilermakers, welcomed the idea of a PWR. When the TUC in September 1989 decided by over a million votes' majority to seek to phase out nuclear power in fifteen years, this must have come as a bitter blow to the trade unions at Sellafield, who run a campaign called the Nuclear Campaign for the Nuclear Industry. They had successfully lobbied the biggest union, the Transport and General Workers, into changing its anti-nuclear energy policy into one which would embrace nuclear power. As part of their campaign they had sent a report to the Labour Party National Executive Committee saying that the Labour policy of reducing nuclear power would endanger 11,000 jobs at least in the Copeland area, and many others besides in associated industries.

In fact the unions waited until the second week of the county council elections before giving out their report. The plan was to embarrass the Labour councillors into rejecting national party policy. As it happened the Copeland Labour councillors still got voted in, some with increased majorities. Perhaps the public was more concerned with the idea of the planned national nuclear dump NIREX had proposed for Sellafield, another scheme the unions welcomed with few provisos. In fact the unions have backed BNFL in the company's bid to take the extra 4,000 tonnes of reprocessing from Germany.

There are things which stifle the free flow of information on Sellafield. One factor is the Official Secrets Act, but the presence of the UKAEA police force, who enforce the nuclear rulebook, is also a powerful element. In 1976, Tony Benn, the Energy Minister, sponsored the Special Constables Act through Parliament. This legislation was to enable a police force which could safeguard the 'plutonium economy' which THORP was initiating. It was not only the 'woolly hat and jumper' brigade who were having serious misgivings about an energy policy which needed attendant armed guards – politicians and bureaucrats were also worried. The Royal Commission Report of 1976 voiced grave misgivings about embarking on a power programme which was dependent on plutonium as its primary fuel.

The 650 strong UKAEA police came under fire in 1983 from Liberal MP Alan Beith: 'Civil police forces have a system of accountability when armed. They are responsible to a Chief Constable and through him to a local police committee. There are established procedures for considering the policy of the force. The UKAEA runs its police force quite independently of all this. It is only responsible to the Secretary of State for Industry in a very diffuse way. The police can work outside nuclear facilities and have the power to search and use arms. They can enter your home armed even if you are not a Windscale employee. I believe there is a danger in police carrying arms and it is even greater without controls. In the strict sense they are a private police force, the only armed private police force in the country.' (w/n 1.12.83).

The issue of security for nuclear installations was raised at the Windscale inquiry. Someone had written a fictional account of how terrorists could get into a plant like Sellafield and steal plutonium. BNFL issued a statement saying, 'Security arrangements at Windscale are devised with the supervision and cooperation of the Government security organisations. They are satisfied and regularly reviewed. The government and the authorities concerned are satisfied that the security measures now in force or planned are adequate for present circumstances.' The Windscale Inquiry heard from the then Managing Director of BNFL, Con Allday, that terrorists could steal plutonium and make a crude bomb, but that it would be difficult. The questioning had arisen because a calculation showed that the Sellafield plutonium stockpile was seven and a half tonnes. Reprocessing in THORP would increase that stockpile to forty-five tonnes by the year 2000. Allday was asked if plutonium was stored in a country was it possible that terrorists might take it? Allday said it was possible, but not very likely. Kidwell, Friends of the Earth QC, asked Allday, 'Would it be possible to manufacture a nuclear bomb?' Allday replied that, although he would not like to be explicit, he thought it could be made (tel 21.6.77).

In 1982 the trial of Gerard Tuite gave everyone a surprise. Tuite was the first IRA man to be extradited from the north to the south of Ireland to stand charge. On a tape found in Tuite's flat a spent fuel train carrying nuclear waste to Windscale was described as a target. The information was included with a 'hit list' of twenty-five prominent politicians. Cryptic pieces of information were given on the tape. The reference to Windscale was described as 'information received'. The transportation of nuclear waste from two points in northern England and the Scottish border involved 'target railway tracks to Windscale from Whitehaven and Barrow-in-Furness'. These were not amateurs either, as the politician Airey Neave who was assassinated in 1979 by a booby trap bomb in his car was on the same hit list (g 7.7.82).

In October 1987 an international black-marketeer told the world how he had seen consignments of plutonium on sale in unofficial 'world armaments market' (g 30.10.87).

In June 1984 a very strange, but not unique incident happened. Contaminated overalls were found hidden in a changing room at Sellafield, at the same time as other 'radioactive material' was found. The UKAEA police mounted an investigation. BNFL admitted that the material gave off levels of radiation 'significantly higher than those normally found in an area like this. It was contaminated and had obviously been concealed. The firm are looking on this very seriously. The material was no use to anybody, but someone had obviously broken the rules and that is why the incident is being taken so seriously (w/n 28.6.84, e/m 28.6.84). It took BNFL a year to report the outcome of the investigations. The company suspected that the radioactive material had been left in the changing room so as to 'nobble' another worker. In fact after further investigation it was decided that the man who had worn the contaminated clothing would have received a dose twice that of the yearly limit. The company described the dose as 'massive'. The radioactive material had been placed in the man's pocket after the alarms in the changing room had been turned off. The victim had been in line for promotion, something he would not get 'out of the area'. BNFL admitted, 'Active liquor sample bottles were found and it looks as if someone had deliberately contaminated the overalls.' (g 19.6.85).

Over the years quite a number of things have been stolen from Sellafield; like any big factory it is subject to pilfering. This does not make Sellafield workers any less honest than most workers. In Barrow the joke is that if Vickers took back all that belonged to them the town would fall apart. For most working men the 'appropriation' of company goods is seen as a perk of the job. As one man told me: 'Those in the offices get company cars, less radiation and work shorter hours. We get things we need for the home.' Petty pilfering has, over the years, given way to a more dangerous game, that of taking material home which should have gone to Drigg. Workers have taken tools and overalls out of the radioactive area and sold contaminated materials or kept them for their own use. New changing rooms prevent much of this sort of pilfering happening now. However, there are still ways in which such articles can be brought off the site, as not all the changing rooms that workers go through have compulsory monitoring. One worker told me, 'I would always do it when there's a police woman on the gate, because I know she's not going to give me a body search'. The same worker added, 'Because there's so much contamination around Sellafield the radiation alarms are not set to zero, so most of the stuff won't set the alarms off. I only stopped when I had kids, because I didn't want them playing with it.'

In December 1987 George Brown, an employee at Sellafield, had his home raided by BNFL and local police. Apparently they waited until he left home before they swooped. It seems they were in search of a canister of radioactive material which had gone missing from the plant, but after checking Brown's home with Geiger counters they found no unusually high levels of radiation. Brown told reporters, 'Obviously I know all about the dangers of radioactive material. Do you think I would endanger my own home? (dm 2.12.70). Brown was sacked not long afterwards. He was accused of deliberately dosing himself with radiation. After a routine body monitor had shown he had above normal levels of contamination he was withdrawn from work in the active area, but his levels still continued to rise. Brown did not appeal against this sacking (w/n 10/12/87). I asked one worker why anyone might do such a thing. 'A number of reasons really, unhappy with working in the area, worried that you are going to be put on a really radioactive job in a Windscale suit, or, hopes that you might be put out but still get the same rate of pay. If the company rules or equipment are found to be at fault you still get active area money for working in the clean areas. I think that this sort of thing would not happen in a chemical plant because they know the effects of certain chemical substances would be too immediate, i.e. you'd kill yourself there and then. But with radiation, and here we're all to blame, you think a lot of little doses over a period of time might not even harm you and if it does, so what, they pay out on cancers don't they?'

The psychology report we leaked in 1985 started with the following paragraph: 'In a plant like Windscale, where not only accidents occur, but workers have been known to expose themselves intentionally to excessive levels of radiation to earn a few days' sick leave off work, management clearly have to maintain an awareness of "psychological" aspects of the work which goes on there.'

Brown's brush with BNFL's police was not the first for a Sellafield worker. In November 1980 the General Municipal and Boilermakers considered taking a case against the UKAEA police for possible infringement of civil liberties. An unnamed changing room attendant, aged sixty-one, had been taken from his workplace, subjected to two hours' interrogation and pressurised into signing an authorisation for the police to search his home. Throughout what was described as a 'heavy-handed interrogation' the man had no legal representation. So scared was the worker that it was a week later before he could bring himself to tell the union what had happened. The union hit out at the police, a spokesman saying, 'The methods and manner in which they went about their business had raised some serious questions in the minds of the trade unions on site and have given cause for concern about what the rights of all employees at Windscale are. This man was an elderly worker who had never been in a police court in his life and he was extremely upset by the whole thing.' The police search, sparked off by malicious information, did not reveal any stolen items. The UKAEA police can enter any premises at will and have the power to arrest on suspicion (w/n Nov. 1980). In June 1981 3,000 workers went on strike when UKAEA police searched the homes of two process workers after an anonymous tip-off had said that stolen property was being hidden in their houses. The union's anger was directed at the police because, unlike the civil police, they had acted on unsubstantiated evidence when taking their action. The UKAEA police responded by issuing a leaflet to all workers informing them of their rights (w/n 1.6.81). The UKAEA searches took place without warrants. Tools belonging to the company were found in one of the houses searched.

We know that files are kept on people. Bob Burton, another one of BNFL's PR men, told me that he had seen their file on me. Even after questions were asked in the House BNFL refused to release the file itself, saying that it was just press clippings. Burton, though, had given the game away by mentioning something that I had never told the press before.

In August 1986 Christine Merlin and I went to a meeting in Broughton where Ministry of Agriculture officials were giving a presentation on Chernobyl. We both went in Christine's car. Driving home Christine found that the nuts holding the car tyres on had been loosened. This must have been done whilst we were inside the meeting hall. Whoever had done it had obviously wanted to cause Christine or myself serious harm, especially as the drive home is along small country roads, some of which have a sheer drop on the side. On the way home the Merlins two young boys were in the car as well.

Strange as it may seem one of the most laughable episodes in the campaign came when we first met up with the UKAEA police in June 1981. CORE had planned a demonstration in Workington against the first shipment of plutonium nitrate to travel from Dounreay to Sellafield. As the only people with any experience of direct action we had gone to give advice and help on what to do when the ship came in. The night before the action we had found that the narrowest point in the road leading from the docks was a small hump-backed bridge with a wrought-iron fence on either side. It could not have been more ideal, as our plan was to put a chain across the road and handcuff people to it.

The next day was dry and clear. Quite a good-sized crowd had gathered to give the protesters support. The ship eventually docked, by this time spray painted by people in a small dinghy who had rowed alongside. Then the terrible moment came as the two lorries carrying the huge containers, accompanied by police Land Rovers, sped out of the dock compound. Our cars rushed ahead over the bridge. Out of sight from us other protestors stopped the first of the cars, giving us time to get out of the car. There was only one very civil civilian policeman on the bridge itself. We attached the chain and spread out across the road as the first truck came towards us. What happened next was pure farce. Mark Glover from Greenpeace shouted, 'The chain's too bloody short.' We all immediately sat down. Police and protestors, TV cameramen and photographers all got caught up in the mêlée as we pulled on one end of the chain and the police pulled on the other in a farcical tug-of-war.

Such moderation proved too much for some of the UKAEA police in the Land Rovers, who started kicking and swearing at the people chained up. A car was driven at one person and the door opened to try and knock him over. When the scenes appeared on the national news a stream of protest led the Chief Constable of the County to issue a statement pointing out that his men were not responsible for the violent acts. We later learnt that all the UKAEA police had been armed.

That day holds very bitter-sweet memories for me. After the action we all went for a quiet drink to calm down, and in the same little pub some men from the steel-works were celebrating their redundancies. They thought what we had done was great, but after a few drinks one old guy turned to me and said, 'But a man needs a job, lass. That's why our lads'll be bussing it down to Sellafield from now on.' He had tears in his eyes.

In 1990 it doesn't seem particularly strange to see people protesting at environmental damage. But nine years ago Greenpeace was the extreme of the eco-movement and protest took place mostly around committee tables. I will never be able to say what caught my imagination so much that I gave up a promising career and took a life of conflict with officialdom. I was not born to protest. Nice Catholic girls who go to convents aren't. I have been asked on numerous occasions why I took this job. The pay is low, the hours are lousy. But the company I keep is the finest in the world. My only answer for this seeming madness is that I love Cumbria and its people. For all their good and bad points it's home and I feel that the past ten years have been worth all the effort if in some small way I have helped to keep it safer.

But having said that I am soon to leave England to go and work in Australia for a while. After ten years I feel entitled to take a break. I want to live in a country where I can look at the sea and not have to wonder how much plutonium there is in it. I want to breathe the air without having to think how much americium I am gulping in. When BNFL contaminated the Irish Sea they committed a crime against the environment. They took away from the people of Cumbria something that they hold very dear. And I will never forgive them for that.

But I am not leaving because I feel we have lost the argument over Sellafield and nuclear power. Or because I feel that we are facing such overwhelming odds that we will never win. Quite the contrary. I am leaving because I think we have made such strides forward that the time has come to be able to take a rest from the frontline. The successes in certain parts of the anti-nuclear campaign have been complete. The nuclear dump sites certainly won their battles. Greenpeace managed to get the seamen to stop dumping nuclear waste at sea. The view on nuclear power itself does not seem that good as the Government is still ordering reactors. However, Margaret Thatcher's promise to order one new reactor for every term of her office has failed to materialise. The first one, Sizewell B, is not yet complete. In fact due to environmental pressure for stricter safety and better discharge control the Conservatives are closing Bradwell and Hunterston B. The Fast Breeder Reprocessing plant at Dounreay has fallen victim to market forces. Even at Sellafield there has been success. The company has been made to clean up its sea discharges. Campaigns on the effects of radiation have seen a lowering of the recommended limits. Even Drigg is being cleaned up.

It took the terrible tragedy of Chernobyl to make the public as a whole realise what we meant when we said nuclear power and its hazards are unique. The nuclear empire is slowly decaying but the legacy it leaves will be cursed by generations yet to come.

EPILOGUE

- At the Merlins' court case Mr Geoffrey Webb, secretary to the National Radiological Protection Board, admitted that the radiation dose which would keep members of the public within 'acceptable risk limits' is 0.2 mSv. The present recommended level stands at 0.5 mSv. On the same day he admitted that new evidence on the uptake of plutonium and americium from contaminated food could lead to members of the public receiving higher doses than previously thought. Those most at risk would be people eating fish and shellfish from the Irish Sea. For the year 1981 the recalculated radiation dose for such a person would have been 14 mSv, not 3.65 mSv as previously published.
- It was revealed during the court case that 27 claims for compensation had been put to BNFL by West Cumbrian companies as a result of loss of business due to media publicity concerning the radioactive slick discharged in November 1983. BNFL offered to buy £75 worth of fish a week from one of the claimants, fisherman Paul Pederson Jnr, as he could not sell his catch. The fish BNFL bought would be for use in their canteen at Sellafield.
- Estimates show some seven tonnes of plutonium will go into BNFL's proposed underground dump if it gets the go-ahead.
- After the 1989 Shadow Cabinet elections for the Labour Party Jack Cunningham, the MP for Copeland, became Campaign Co-ordinator instead of spokesman for the Environment.
- Sadly Bill Maxwell died on 7th November as a result of cancer.
- On 9th November the Government decided to build no more PWRs and will take all nuclear plants out of the privatisation programme. The same day BNFL abandoned the first bore-hole for the Sellafield underground dump due to a geological fault.
- Gemma D'Arcy, whose parents are suing BNFL because of their daughter's acute myeloid leukaemia, is still very ill. However, doctors treating her have discovered her father may be a possible bone marrow donor and an operation to save Gemma is planned.

CHRONOLOGY

1947 Go-ahead given to build military Plutonium Piles at Ministry of Supply ammunition factory at Sellafield, West Cumbria. Site renamed Windscale. The radiation limit for a worker stands at 150 milli-Sieverts (mSv) per annum.

1949 Two kilometre pipeline laid in Irish Sea to discharge low level radioctive liquid effluent.

1950 Plutonium Pile No. 1 begins production of plutonium for Britain's first atomic bomb. No. 2 Pile brought on stream in 1951.

1951 Separation plant, B204, used to extract plutonium from spent nuclear fuel, is completed.

1951 In October Britain's first atomic bomb exploded on Montebello Islands, Australia.

1952 A radiation dose of 15 mSv per annum is recommended for members of the public.

1954 United Kingdom Atomic Energy Authority, UKAEA, is formed and takes over nuclear sites from Ministry of Supply. The Dounreay fast-breeder plant is given the go-ahead.

1952–56 Strontium and other radionuclides spread over Cumbrian countryside from burst spent fuel rods in base of Plutonium Piles.

1956 First of four magnox reactors opened by Queen Elizabeth II at Calder Hall. The reactors, hailed as the world's first large-scale nuclear plants, produce plutonium for military purposes. Four magnox reactors also built for military purposes at Chapel Cross in south-west Scotland. The CEGB build civilian magnox stations at eight other sites.

1957 Disastrous fire in Plutonium Pile No. 1 leads to closure of both reactors forever. The recommended level of radiation for a worker is reduced to 50 mSv.

1958 The Windscale Advanced Gas-cooled Reactor, a prototype for commercial AGRs, is started.

1959 Recommended radiation limit for the public reduced to 5 mSv.

216

1964 A new reprocessing plant, B205, is opened to extract uranium and plutonium from spent fuel from magnox reactors.

1966 The Advanced Gas-cooled Reactor programme is started. Eventually only six are built as the programme is delayed and costs overrun.

1969 BNFL begin to notice problem with corrosion of magnox fuel in cooling pond, leading to higher discharges of gamma and beta radionuclides. The same year zeolite skips, to reduce discharges, are fitted in Bradwell nuclear power station.

1971 British Nuclear Fuels Limited is formed as a public limited company to take over fuel fabrication and reprocessing services from UKAEA. BNFL runs the Windscale and Calder Works, Sellafield, the magnox reactors at Chapel Cross in Scotland, the Springfields fuel fabrication plant in Lancashire and the Capenhurst uranium enrichment site in Cheshire. The headquarters are at Risley, near Warrington. The same year BNFL apply to have sea discharge levels for alpha emitters from Sellafield increased from 1,800 curies to 6,000 curies per annum.

1973 The old reprocessing plant, B204, which has been converted to handle spent oxide fuel, has a serious accident. A blow-back of butex gas during experimental reprocessing causes severe contamination of the building. 35 men are seriously contaminated. The plant is never used again. Alpha discharges at their highest. Three-day working week due to industrial action causes backlog of magnox fuel in cooling ponds. Discharges of radioactivity to sea begin to rise.

1974 News of foreign nuclear waste contracts leaked to the press.

1975 Discharges of gamma and beta emitters reach their peak at 250,000 curies.

1976 Proposals to dump nuclear waste near Ennerdale Lake in Cumbria are first mooted. These are later abandoned.

1977 Windscale Inquiry, the first major examination of nuclear reprocessing in the UK, takes place. The hundred-day inquiry hears the evidence for and against the building of the Thermal Oxide Reprocessing Plant (THORP), which will reprocess oxide spent fuel from UK and abroad. The company is hoping an expanded AGR programme, followed by a number of PWRs, will provide the customers for THORP. BNFL install zeolite skips in cooling ponds to reduce beta and gamma emitters.

1978 The go-ahead to build THORP is given.

1979 Proposals to dump nuclear waste in Scotland and Wales are heard at public inquiries. Both plans later abandoned.

1979 Mrs Thatcher becomes Prime Minister and promises to order one nuclear reactor for every year she is in office.

1982 The Political Ecology Research Group issue the first report on the possible health impact of the 1957 Fire. This is followed by a report on the health impact of the Sellafield marine discharges.

1983 January, the National Radiological Protection Board issues its first ever report on the 1957 fire. In September the NRPB recommend BNFL to cut its alpha discharges to 200 curies per annum. In the same month the newly formed NIREX goes to Billingham to attempt to establish a national nuclear dump. November 1st, Yorkshire TV documentary 'Windscale – the Nuclear Laundry' is screened, highlighting high incidence of childhood leukaemias in Seascale and the surrounding area. Government commissions inquiry, the Black Committee, the next day. November 11th, BNFL start to discharge part of radioactive slick into Irish Sea. Monday, 14th, Greenpeace workers monitoring radioactivity levels in seawater detect slick at sea. Sunday, 19th, beaches 'closed', then re-opened the following day for four days. 20th, Greenpeace divers attempt to block pipeline and are subsequently fined £50,000. Thursday, 23rd, warnings given to avoid 'unnecessary' use of the beaches along 20 mile stretch of Cumbrian coast. The AGR at Sellafield is closed.

1984 Beach warning lifted at the end of June 1984. Three days later the Black Report is published. It confirms that childhood leukaemias in Seascale are ten times the national average. Recommended dose limit for the public reduced to 1 mSv.

1985 In July BNFL is found guilty on four criminal charges in the Crown Court in Carlisle as a result of the 1983 'beach incident'. Site Ion Exchange Plant comes on stream to reduce discharges of gamma and beta emitters.

1986 In January the House of Commons Select Committee on the Environment calls for a review of the need for THORP. In April 1986 Chernobyl contaminates most of Europe, including Cumbria, North Wales, Scotland, the Isle of Man and Northern Ireland. In June the Sellafield discharges are legally reduced. The gamma/

beta authorisation is lowered to 26,000 curies per annum and for alpha discharges to 378 curies per annum.

1987 NRPB recommends maximum safe annual radiation dose to workers of 15 mSv. For the public the limit is 1 mSv for all non-medical sources of man-made radioactivity, with a limit of 0.5 mSv from any single installation. In April NIREX announces that it is to abandon attempts to site a nuclear dump in one of four sites in Southern England. In September BNFL announce their plans to investigate having a national nuclear dump at Sellafield.

1988 First authorisation limiting aerial discharges is signed. Government abandons full-scale fast breeder reactor at Dounreay and will close existing facility. COMARE report on Dounreay leukaemias suggest a link between nuclear reprocessing plants and leukaemias in young people living near them.

1989 In March NIREX officially announces that it will investigate the possibility of siting a national nuclear dump at either Dounreay or Sellafield, the sites of Britain's only reprocessing plants. Work begins on a borehole for the underground dump at Sellafield in August. By mid-year all magnox stations are withdrawn from privatisation because they are considered too expensive for private investors. The Inspector who heard evidence into a proposed expansion at Dounreay gives the plan the green light.

1990 In January the Department of the Environment signs an authorisation allowing BNFL to discharge up to 270 curies of alpha emitters per annum, seven years after the NRPB recommended a level of 200 curies.

**The Gaia Atlas of Planet Management
for today's caretakers of tomorrow's world** £14.95
General Editor Norman Myers
foreword by David Bellamy

This book is a definitive guide to a planet in critical transition. How humankind uses Earth's vast resources today will determine the health and ultimately the survival of our complex ecosphere for the decades and centuries to come.

Can we learn to manage our environment? The answer is yes, but in order to do so, we must first understand the fragile interaction and interdependence that link all living things. If this vital balance is not maintained, we face a bleak future – or no future at all.

The facts of our situation and our options for tomorrow are presented in this remarkable atlas. With its wealth of data, vivid graphics, and authoritative text by the leading thinkers on these crucial environmental, political, and social issues, *The Gaia Atlas of Planet Management* is both an important resource and an impassioned challenge for anyone concerned with the welfare of our world.

'This atlas is the vanguard of a new generation. It looks at the world in a new, mature light, its vision . . . fired with a new understanding . . . It should take its place not only in libraries and homes, but also on board-room and committee-room tables.' DAVID BELLAMY

'This extraordinary and vitally important book explains our place on this planet and the damage we are doing to ourselves . . . It is, in fact, a sort of blueprint for our survival . . . for it shows how we can mend our ways to advantage . . . I wonder what the attitude will be if, in a hundred years time, this book is read by our starving grandchildren – and they see that the decimation of their inheritance was recognized, that cures for it were available, and yet still nothing was done?' GERALD DURRELL

The Gaia Peace Atlas
Survival into the Third Millennium £10.95
Foreword by Javier Pérez de Cuéllar
Secretary-General to the United Nations

This book is a call to action. With the escalation of the arms race and the ecological decline that has accompanied it, humanity is now entering what may prove to be the most crucial epoch of all. Peace is more than the absence of war, and true security cannot be won by arms. As an harmonious relationship between humanity and our life-sustaining planet is coming to be recognized as the only path to a secure future, the decisions we make at this stage are vital to our ultimate survival.

Edited by Dr Frank Barnaby, former director of the Stockholm International Peace Research Institute, *The Gaia Peace Atlas* is a challenging study of the prospects for peace into the next millennium. With research from world-wide organizations and contributions from major international figures – East, West and non-aligned – it presents the options for peace and a sustainable future in authoritative and hard-hitting graphic style.

'Almost a thousand billion dollars are expended each year on arms and armed forces . . . The wanton extravagance of the arms race is apparent from the fact that its expense exceeds the total income of the poorer half of humanity . . . The damage to the natural environment is also serious, and at times irreparable. How utterly senseless it is that precious non-renewable resources should be used to build weapons that may destroy more of these same resources if they are ever used.

Ultimately, it is the peoples of the world who must save themselves. It is my hope that this fine volume will make a significant contribution to knowledge on the interrelated goals of international security, disarmament and sustainable economic growth . . . These goals are both urgent and achievable.'
JAVIER PÉREZ de CUÉLLAR, Secretary-General to the United Nations

All Pan books are available at your local bookshop or newsagent, or can be ordered direct from the publisher. Indicate the number of copies required and fill in the form below.

Send to: **CS Department, Pan Books Ltd., P.O. Box 40, Basingstoke, Hants. RG21 2YT.**

or phone: 0256 469551 (Ansaphone), quoting title, author and Credit Card number.

Please enclose a remittance* to the value of the cover price plus: 60p for the first book plus 30p per copy for each additional book ordered to a maximum charge of £2.40 to cover postage and packing.

*Payment may be made in sterling by UK personal cheque, postal order, sterling draft or international money order, made payable to Pan Books Ltd.

Alternatively by Barclaycard/Access:

Card No.

Signature:

Applicable only in the UK and Republic of Ireland.

While every effort is made to keep prices low, it is sometimes necessary to increase prices at short notice. Pan Books reserve the right to show on covers and charge new retail prices which may differ from those advertised in the text or elsewhere.

NAME AND ADDRESS IN BLOCK LETTERS PLEASE:

Name————————————————————————

Address————————————————————————

3/87